THE BIRDS OF NOTTINGHAMSHIRE

THE BIRDS OF NOTTINGHAMSHIRE

PAST AND PRESENT

edited by

AUSTEN DOBBS

for

THE TRENT VALLEY BIRD WATCHERS

DAVID & CHARLES

NEWTON ABBOT LONDON

NORTH POMFRET (VT) VANCOUVER

ISBN o 7153 6870

Library of Congress Catalog Card Number 74-15798

© Trent Valley Bird Watchers 1975

Set in 11 on 13pt Garamond and printed in
Great Britain by Latimer Trend & Company Ltd Plymouth
for David & Charles (Holdings) Limited
South Devon House Newton Abbot Devon

Published in the United States of America
by David & Charles Inc North Pomfret
Vermont 05053 USA

Published in Canada by Douglas David & Charles Limited
132 Philip Avenue North Vancouver BC

To all
Trent Valley Bird Watchers
Past, Present and Future

CONTENTS

LIST OF ILLUSTRATIONS

List of Illustrations

MAPS AND DIAGRAMS

INTRODUCTION

Thirty-five years after the formation of the Trent Valley Bird Watchers at East Bridgford the time, 1970, seemed opportune to start work on a book on the birds of Nottinghamshire, linking this day and age with what was known of the past, and so achieve one of the main aims of the Society. I was appointed to draft out the format and write the chapters with the help of members whenever it was needed.

As more and more people became interested in birds, a need arose for a source of information under one cover. In Nottinghamshire, after Joseph Whitaker's work to 1907, the information on county birds became fragmentary until the publication of the TVBW annual bird reports from 1942. These, produced in limited numbers, became unobtainable. More Nottinghamshire birdwatchers asked for, or wanted, more background information which they could only obtain with great difficulty—hence this book, which will provide a foundation for future study as well as put local ornithology into perspective for new birdwatchers.

For the ornithology of the 19th century Whitaker is heavily drawn upon to capture the spirit of those leisurely times when lords and gentry kept sporting estates, and daily bags of game took the place of, or equalled, talk on cricket and other sport. Because rare birds were shot and stuffed for collections, the taxidermist was a familiar member of town society, and all kinds of people were prepared to kill a strange bird because its carcase represented ready cash. Sterland of Edwinstowe played a useful role, while the lists of Nottinghamshire birds compiled by W. Felkin in 1866 and F. B. Whitlock in 1893 also gave information from the distant past.

After the publication of his main county bird book, *Notes on the Birds of Nottinghamshire*, in 1907, Whitaker continued to correspond and record, thereby providing useful information right into the period of least recording, when there was no successor to carry on the work. During the 1920s, the period up to the beginnings of TVBW records, ornithologists came at times from other counties to fill in for Nottinghamshire, because there were so few active within the county to make surveys. Without doubt, these years were just as interesting as those which had gone before and those which came after, but hardly anyone recorded, or if they did, their observations were lost.

From 1935 the TVBW took over and, following World War II, increased in membership to make the recording of Nottinghamshire birdlife a full-scale effort.

NOTE

Density of Bird Populations

Because this book spans two centuries, from the middle of the nineteenth until well into the twentieth, English acreage has been used, reflecting those times when the hectare was not locally known. A standard of 100 acres has been adopted wherever possible, a measurement which like the span and the stride is within the range of understanding. It represents five or six fields of farmland or a large wood, units well within the visual comprehension of the field ornithologist. For those interested, 100 acres represents 40·4 hectares. Also, 1 square mile equals 2·5 square kilometres.

NOTTINGHAMSHIRE
ORNITHOLOGISTS

As with most studies of natural history we begin the history of Nottinghamshire birds at the time of John Ray (1627–1705), and since they are Nottinghamshire birds we couple him with Francis Willughby of Wollaton. Whitaker will have it that 'all the honour that has been given to Ray, so far as it concerns systematic zoology, belongs exclusively to him' (Willughby); a rather comprehensive statement. These two great scientific friends undertook much research together which has become the basis of all our present knowledge. According to James Fisher (*Shell Bird Book*, 1966) on the Willughby-Ray *Ornithologia* 1676 (English version 1678), these two Stuart period naturalists even showed awareness of some difficult species—wood warbler and chiffchaff, redpoll and twite for instance. It would have been a fine start for a book on Nottinghamshire ornithology if we had possessed something personal by Willughby on the birds of his home surroundings at Wollaton Hall.

From this time until the middle of the 19th century those interested in birds in the county were mainly noted for their collections of birds or birds' eggs. Francis Foljambe (1750–1814) of Osberton had a fine collection which is still preserved at

Osberton. He was a friend of G. Montague, the author of the *Dictionary of British Birds* 1814, who named the little crake, Gallinula Foljambei, after him. This rare visitor to Britain has since been renamed. Foljambe found it in a poulterer's shop in London.

John Wolley (1823–59) was the son of the Vicar of Beeston. He was a great traveller and besides visiting Tangier and Mont Blanc did much exploration on the northern nesting grounds. Starting with Orkney, Shetland and Faroe (he wrote 'Birds of Faroe' in Sir William Jardine's *Contributions to Ornithology*), he reached Lapland, where he wintered in 1853, and spent some summers exploring the Varangar Fjord and Lake Inari. He visited the Baltic Islands, being the first ornithologist to find the nest and eggs of the waxwing and nesting site of the smew, and he went to Iceland on an abortive search for the great auk.

F. B. Whitlock, who wrote the *Birds of Derbyshire* in 1893, also lived at Beeston, and his egg collection is at the Wollaton Hall Museum. He also wrote a 'Check-list of Nottinghamshire Birds' in 1893 which was included in *A Contribution to the Geology and Natural History of Nottinghamshire* (J. W. Carr). Other keen 19th-century collectors mentioned by Whitaker are William Felkin of Beeston, who wrote the report on Birds for the Nottingham meeting of the British Association 1866; H. Pearson of Bramcote, another traveller in northern Europe; F. B. Footitt, the Newark coroner; H. F. Walter of Papplewick, the possessor of a great auk's egg, and J. Chaworth Musters of Annesley Park.

W. J. Sterland, author of *The Birds of Sherwood Forest* (1869), seems to have been a rather different type of man. Though he occasionally used his gun he had no large collection of birds, and was more a naturalist than a sportsman. He did, however, have a good egg collection. He was born at Ollerton in 1815, the son of William Sterland, ironmonger, grocer and chandler. It is thought he went to Australia for a time, but he was back in Ollerton in 1837, and took charge of the business on his father's death in 1853. His name appears as churchwarden 1855, but after 1864 it disappears from the list of tradesmen, and he had presumably retired

VICE-COUNTY OF NOTTINGHAMSHIRE

Finningley
Misson
West Stockwith
Bawtry
Misterton
Mattersey
Blyth
Lound
Bole
Worksop
East Retford
Littleborough
Cottam
WELBECK
CLUMBER
Carburton
Dunham
Thorney
Warsop
Tuxford
Edwinstowe
Weston
Girton
CLIPSTONE FOREST
Rufford
Ossington
Besthorpe
Kneesall
Cromwell
Mansfield
North Muskham
Sutton-in-Ashfield
Kirklington
South Muskham
Huthwaite
Blidworth
Farnsfield
Winthorpe
Kirkby-in-Ashfield
Newark
Southwell
NEWSTEAD ABBEY
Oxton
East Stoke
Hucknall
Hoveringham
Bulwell
Arnold
Gunthorpe
Netherfield
Nottingham
Colwick
Bingham
Beeston
Holme Pierrepoint
West Bridgford
Colston Bassett
Attenborough
Cotgrave
Gotham
West Leake
Widmerpool
Wysall

0   10
Miles

to indulge in more congenial occupations. He lived in a house next to the mill, and died in the early 1880s.

W. J. Sterland was at school at Wilford, and it seems possible that this may have been the sort of small private school where the teacher was able to bring out the qualities of an intelligent boy. Certainly *The Birds of Sherwood Forest* has an ease and charm of style that makes it pleasant reading even today. A long introductory chapter deals first with the history of the Sherwood Forest, its ancient oak trees and its great houses, and then with its general natural history. The geology is outlined, and a description given of the habitats of birds, the lakes and woodlands and their salient plant communities, by one who was obviously a fine all-round naturalist. He observed a plant named *Vicia lathroides* (spring vetch), which is far from obvious or easy to identify, but yet very typical of the Forest. Just occasionally, as with the black redstart, his collecting zeal engulfed his natural bent for accuracy.

His following seven chapters deal with 172 species of birds, arranged according to their type—Perching Birds, Game Birds, Water Birds, etc. It is not a list. The species are arranged in order, each followed by its Latin name, but the descriptions and notes on habitat and occurrence follow the author's fancy. The book is anecdotal, with descriptions of pigeons' nests built of nails, and thrushes, blackbirds, and flycatchers following each other in using the same one nest, but the tone of the writing is always scientific; Sterland was an accurate observer, and it never degenerated into sloppy nature mush.

There are four illustrations drawn by Sterland himself, one line drawing of trees, and three birds in colour. The colours are beautifully blended and the texture of the feathers almost visible on the page. In the picture of the bantam the small details of the farmyard are rendered in Bewick's style; it is a great pity no more of his drawings survive. The book was first published in *The Field* in 1865 and 1867. Sterland also wrote a volume on *Mammals* for the Handbook of Natural History series and *A Descriptive List of the Birds of Nottinghamshire* in conjunction with J. Whitaker. This work of 71 pages is a list of 238 species, each with the scientific and common name, followed by notes on frequency, habitat and behaviour.

Joseph Whitaker was born in 1850, the son of Joseph Whitaker of Ramsdale Farm near Arnold, who owned some considerable property there and at Blyth. He was essentially a showman, and with eighty-two years of life before him, used every opportunity to display his talent. In White's *Directory* 1879, we find him recorded as farmer of Rainworth Cottage, Blidworth. By 1885 Rainworth Lodge was listed among the 'seats of the nobility and gentry', and in the list for Blidworth it is quoted as the residence of 'Joseph Whitaker, Esq., J.P., F.Z.S.' and the home of his famous ornithological collections. He lived here for fifty years and built up what must have been a small wonderland. When he died he was buried in the 'Happy Valley' in the park, in a stone receptacle built in the form of a small dwelling.

The house is in one of those small wooded valleys full of willow, alder and oak trees so typical of Sherwood Forest. There is a steep wooded bank to the south, dropping to a marshy bottom with a small clear stream running over a pebble bed. Coming down from Fountain Dale, and falling into L Lake just across the road, the stream has been widened into a small sinuous lake. Nowadays, due to water extraction from the sandstone, the stream can be of uncertain flow.

The house, of which parts are ancient (it purports to be on the site of one of the old Forest hunting lodges), faces partly towards the lake, and partly up the valley towards an old stone barn. Whitaker had the lake wired to house his collection of waterfowl, which were quite tame and took food from his hand or the cook's. He also managed to use part of the lake for two duck decoys, or traps, from which he obtained much amusement. The owner of L Lake allowed him to study the birds there, and he later acquired an area of marsh close by for waders. Behind the house he had his 'bird walk', an acre of land with a bird box in every tree. Each bird had its own type of architecture, a (presumably stone) hot-water bottle with the stopper removed for blue tits, an erection of a portico with a flower-pot saucer base for flycatchers, and so on.

The land rises very steeply some fifteen feet immediately behind the house and at the top was the deer park, a piece of pleasant rolling forest country of 22 acres well sheltered by belts of pine. Here he ran twenty-one fallow deer which he said did extremely well on light land. For company they had ten four-horned St Kilda sheep, two rheas and three emus.

The famous collection of stuffed birds, the remains of which are at the Mansfield Museum, numbered 113 specimens in 1904 and, by his death, had grown to 520 birds and 52 animals. There is a description of its early growth in *Scribblings of a Hedgerow Naturalist*. At that time the birds were practically all British though not all from Nottinghamshire. He specialised in albino forms. Clifford Borrer, on one of Whitaker's visits to him at Cowfold, had suggested specialisation in varieties as a way of sustaining his interest in collecting. People came from all over the country to see it and the Visitors' Book, started in 1881, includes everyone from the Duke of Portland to the Nottingham Field Science Club, well-known ornithologists and writers of country faunas include Aplin, Harting, Haines and others. The assembly and maintenance of such a collection involved an immense amount of correspondence and much of this, letters to fellow-ornithologists, to people offering specimens, and to the equerries to the King and the King of Portugal, is preserved at the Mansfield Library. The separate letters are filed in folders according to their subject, and it is obvious from, for example, the file on the alpine chough, that Whitaker went to great lengths to determine the species and also to ascertain the true provenance of records.

His writings are easy to read, giving a pleasant period picture while avoiding a heavy period style. In 1879 he published *A Descriptive List of the Birds of Nottinghamshire* with W. J. Sterland. The *Notes on the Birds of Nottinghamshire* (1907) gives the common name, scientific name and local names where these exist. This is followed by information on the distribution of each species in the county, with notes on its habits and habitat in a rather more chatty style than modern printing costs will allow. He also noted any aberrants such as albinos. The Introduction gives a very brief description of the county and a history of previous workers. Whitaker was a compulsive writer and among his various works on subjects from deer parks to dovecotes was a book on *British Duck Decoys* (1918) and a *Duck Flighting Table* produced in 1921. A Fellow of the Zoological Society and Vice-President of the Selbourne Society, he was popular with all ranks of life, particularly the surrounding miners to whom he gave racing tips. He was, above all, an all-round countryman. He was indeed devoted to all field sports, a keen fisherman and a fine shot, being a gun in the famous shoot at Berry Hill, Mansfield, on 10 September 1906 when 1,504 partridges were shot. This may, in our compartmentalised and sentimental age, seem incongruous with his character as a naturalist, but he lived in a time when instincts were broader, perhaps more primitive. His activities as one of the old-time collectors added much to our knowledge, without his findings the present book would be very poor indeed on local 19th-century ornithology.

In recent times two men deserve a mention, as the tide of amateur ornithology began to flow strongly in Britain: Arthur Mason, of East Bridgford, who founded the Trent Valley Bird Watchers in 1935, and Jack Staton, the society's vigorous secretary, who from 1942 to 1954 began the systematic recording of Nottinghamshire birdlife which paved the way for this book. Both these naturalists were known to the general public through their writings in the *Nottingham Guardian*.

As more people became interested in birds, wider studies involving teamwork became possible, and so, from Jack Staton's time onward, there developed organised group work of various kinds. Our local ringers, who operated on a small scale by ringing nestlings and working garden traps, gradually merged into groups, especially from the inception of the mist-net, which demanded more than one handler. Two or more nets were more productive than one, and therefore the development of ringing groups followed naturally. Numbers of birds ringed annually in Nottinghamshire rose from a few hundreds to 5,273 by 1960, and to around 10,000 for 1970, when the Fairham Comprehensive

School Ornithological Society worked the south-western corner of the county, the Attenborough Ringing Group controlled the western gateway of the Trent Valley, and the initial members of what became the Dukeries Group operated in Old Sherwood and district. Others continued to work alone, including ringers who came to Nottinghamshire from Yorkshire.

Although haphazard ringing continued, there was a marked change in approach when specific objectives were aimed for, such as the Population Study of Reed Buntings, Reed Warblers and Sedge Warblers at Attenborough, the concentrated work on our Canada Geese, and the intensive ringing of the Sand Martin. Here, once again, the changes locally reflected the development of ringing throughout Britain, and possibly 1970 marked the beginning of the end of the casual ringing of any bird which came along, except where doing so helped to train another ringer. In future, to make the most of the manpower available, to use the rings economically as regards cost and results, and to achieve worthwhile objectives quickly, ringing will be carefully planned and organised almost like a military campaign.

Groups have also been used for various field studies such as the Winter Wildfowl Counts which, along with the Heronry Census, are classic examples of what can be achieved by amateur bird-watchers working together. The Rookery Counts carried out by the TVBW for 1958 and 1962 played a vital part in the campaign against the use of the new, deadly poisons of the chlorinated hydrocarbons group. Now this teamwork has been used for the national *Bird Atlas* which places modern ornithology far from those distant days when Francis Willughby first watched the birds in Wollaton Park in the 17th century.

NOTTINGHAMSHIRE—GEOLOGY AND TOPOGRAPHY

Nottinghamshire is usually classed as one of the East Midland counties, although in many ways it belongs to and is treated as a northern area of the Midlands—especially where weather forecasting is concerned, or if one is studying the distribution of the nightingale or whooper swan!

For size, Nottinghamshire can be classed as average because, with its 844 square miles, it holds a central placing among the counties of England and Wales. At its greatest it is some 52 miles long and 27 miles wide, bounded by Derbyshire to the west, Yorkshire to the north, Lincolnshire to the east and Leicestershire to the south.

It can be described as lowland in character, and yet its western area near Huthwaite and Moorgreen is from 500 to 651 feet, where the Pennines finally lose themselves into a series of escarpments and dip slopes, which slant eastwards. Nottinghamshire, therefore, links the uplands of the Pennines with the lowlands of the east.

The western parts are heavily industrialised and are flanked by the broad stretch of forest country on the sandstone. To the east and south of these lies the wide belt of farmland cut by the important feature of the Trent Valley. Nottinghamshire is of a rough oval shape and the River Trent enters at the south-western corner to flow north-eastwards to Newark before turning abruptly north to leave the county at the north-eastern corner.

A glance at the map on page 22 will reveal that the main topographical features are linked with the geology of the county.

1   COAL MEASURES. Mainly a grazing region with some woodland. A markedly undulating area which straddles the border with

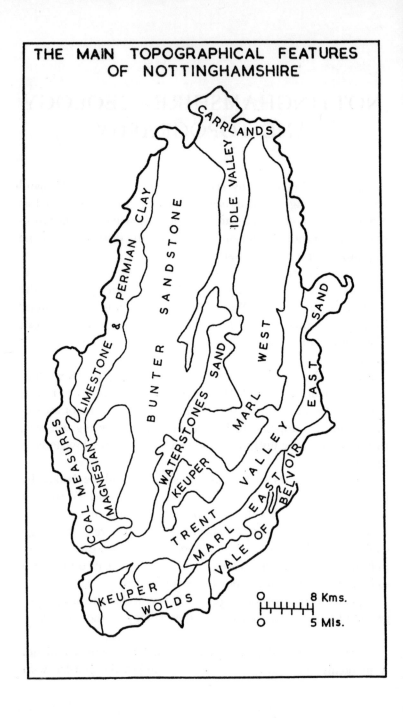

THE MAIN TOPOGRAPHICAL FEATURES
OF NOTTINGHAMSHIRE

CARRLANDS

IDLE VALLEY

LIMESTONE & PERMIAN CLAY

BUNTER SANDSTONE

WEST

SAND

EAST

MARL

WATERSTONES SAND

KEUPER

COAL MEASURES

MAGNESIAN

TRENT VALLEY

MARL EAST

VALE OF BELVOIR

KEUPER

WOLDS

0 ———————— 8 Kms.

0 ———————— 5 Mls.

neighbouring Derbyshire and is some 4 miles wide in Nottingham-shire. The marks of industry, mainly connected with coal, are most evident in the form of pits, slag-heaps old and new, railway sidings and straggling villages. Gradually the old pits are closing down and the unsightly hills of waste are being grassed and afforested.

2 MAGNESIAN LIMESTONE AND PERMIAN CLAY. This narrow strip of country is the highest and most rugged in the county and has much of the bleakness of the Pennines. Grass and woodland are the main features of the scarp areas, while arable farming is chiefly confined to land less disturbed by the limestone outcrops. There is considerable mining settlement.

3 BUNTER SANDSTONE. This area, some 40 miles long and about 8 miles wide, is one of the county's principal features. The un-dulating 'plateau' characterised by dry valleys and general absence of surface drainage, now even drier due to excessive water extraction by the mines, contains the following types of habitat:

   a. Arable fields, arid and stony, with grassland.
   b. Old woodland comprising oak and birch with bracken.
   c. New woodland, the Forestry Commission's coniferous plantations plus many private stands of conifers.
   d. Heathland, either of heather or gorse, and ever-decreasing.
   e. Watered valleys with marshy flats and meadows.
   f. Ducal estates with their fine mixed woodlands, rhododen-drons and lakes.

4 WATERSTONES SAND. This narrow belt possesses qualities of both the Bunter Sandstone and the Keuper Marl, its flaggy sand-stones being interspersed with bands of marl. The fields are more fertile and the woodlands, often on scarp slopes, are well watered and comprise oak, birch, ash, and lime.

5 KEUPER MARL. This area of clay is the main single feature of Nottinghamshire, covering 40% of the county. Although possess-

ing a well-marked escarpment, it has a rather subdued topography. However, where streams have dissected the plateau, the well-defined valleys are very attractive to birdlife. A feature of the smaller streams is that they flow along small ravines or 'dumbles', narrow areas in which trees and bushes grow undisturbed. This delightful area of well-tilled fields and wide grasslands with villages nestling in the valleys, is well-wooded and also carries most of the county's orchard land.

6   THE VALE OF TRENT. Although this zone is almost entirely in the Keuper Marl (it is a shallow trough often 2 miles wide with a floor of gravel and alluvium), it is important in its own right, and certainly so from an ornithological point of view. The well-wooded cliffs, present for great distances at one side or the other of the valley, are natural highways for many passerine migrants, while on the floor, are gravel pits, reed and osier beds, flood pools, marshy meadows and washland which are attractive to breeding and migratory species.

7   THE WOLDS. The south has an area of Boulder Clay which continues into Leicestershire as an undulating plateau. It is mainly of grassland interspersed by fox coverts and thickets. On the Clipstone and Cotgrave parts of this area the land is more sandy where plantations, both private and Forestry Commission, are located.

8   VALE OF BELVOIR. This is the area of Lower Lias, a mixture of shaggy blue shales and limestone which weathers to a sticky clay. The Vale is a lovely area which was once mainly grassland, but in recent years there has been considerable change to arable. An abundant birdlife is supported by the wealth of hedgerow timber, coverts, thickets and woods, but in some parts the uprooting of the hedgerows is now very evident. Two outliers of the Lias, well away from the Vale, must be mentioned because these are important places for woodland species—the West Leake and Gotham Hills.

9   EAST SAND. Here blown sand and gravel have covered the Lias clay, giving a landscape similar to the Bunter Sandstone; poor arable fields, woodland and heath.

10   THE IDLE VALLEY. The River Idle, formed by the tributaries of the Maun, Meden, and Poulter, and later by the Ryton, joins the Trent at Stockwith. For the bird-watcher its sluggish course (it is well named) represents marshy meadows, gravel pits, and some flood washlands.

11   CARR-LANDS. This area is closely associated with the Idle Valley: it is low-lying carr, or fen, land, and the Nottinghamshire part is the southern fringe of the more extensive Isle of Axholme and Hatfield Chase which was once a place of meres, watercourses, reed beds and marshes. The area is intensively cultivated and the fields are bounded by well-kept drains where hedges are virtually non-existent.

HABITATS

There always has been change, and land usage will continue to adjust to the times. Farming was introduced to Britain by the Neolithic tribes and the first 'fields' of Nottinghamshire may have been created during these early times. However, the first impact on the forest and the creation of what can be called the farmland habitat probably occurred during the Bronze Age, when clearings in the forest were made by burning and felling in order to use the fertile soil much as some primitive tropical forest tribes do today. The Romans too created more farmland, and by then the forest was in retreat in our county. This retreat must have become a rout when the Saxons and the Danes settled here, using efficient iron tools to attack the trees and the plough to turn the soil. The open-field system of these times saw the development of the mixed farm community, with the field species of birds, such as skylark and lapwing, obtaining more habitat, and with some woodland-edge species colonising wherever a thicket barrier provided cover.

The present pattern of the Nottinghamshire farming landscape with its field divisions of hedgerows enhanced by trees came as a result of the enclosure movement. As early as 1517 the commissioners of Henry VIII reported that nearly 2,500 acres were enclosed in the county, and this filling-in of an open countryside continued, slowly at first and then more rapidly towards 1700, accelerating during the 18th century. It is considered that more than 75% of the total area of the county had been enclosed by 1800. Therefore, from an ornithological point of view, there have been some 170 settled years of this type of farmland habitat.

Down the long years the farming has always been mixed, and still is; and the pattern of crops interspersed with pasture has been used by the farmland birds for so long that it is a well-established order. Of course there have been variations in the amounts of arable and pasture; the chart (shown below), shows the changes in acreage of land under crops or grass caused mainly by economic factors acting upon farming policy. A steady fall in arable land took place from c 1850 until 1941 when the process was reversed, and now even areas which became largely grassland, such as the Vale of Belvoir, the South Wolds and the Coal Measures zones, are being changed by the plough.

Possibly, from the farmland bird's point of view, the time of the horse-drawn plough and the use of wholesome manure was the best. Years of artificial fertilisers do not appear to have been harmful, but increased mechanisation has certainly made ground-nesting more hazardous, while the introduction of modern herbicides and pesticides has reduced the amount of animal food,

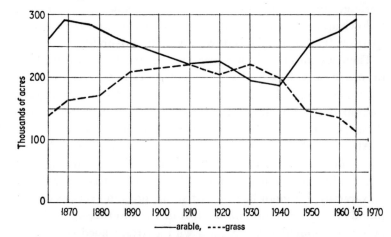

Changes in the acreage of arable and grassland

which is vital as a protein supply for the healthy growth of the chicks.

Economic pressure since the war has seen the disappearance of many small fields and, consequently, the loss of much cover used by farmland birds. In a few places, as yet, the new open landscape has an alien look—hence the name 'prairie farming'—and yet it is really a return to the Nottinghamshire landscape of the years before the enclosures! However, in the early 1970s the county is still very much a land of fields, a mixture of grass and arable, the hedgerows of varying sizes and the trees, viewed from one of the many ridges or escarpment edges, giving the countryside a pleasant, varied, full look and sheltering a well-established bird community.

The breeding species of this community, those likely to be found on a mixed farm are: kestrel, red-legged partridge, common partridge, quail, pheasant, lapwing, stock dove, wood-pigeon, turtle dove, collared dove, cuckoo, barn owl, little owl, tawny owl, long-eared owl, green woodpecker, skylark, swallow, house martin, carrion crow, rook, jackdaw, magpie, wren, mistle thrush, song thrush, blackbird, robin, whitethroat, lesser white-throat, dunnock, meadow pipit, pied wagtail, yellow wagtail, starling, greenfinch, goldfinch, linnet, bullfinch, chaffinch, yellowhammer, reed bunting, corn bunting, house sparrow, tree sparrow. The corncrake is now only a rare possibility.

There are also certain woodland species (such as great tit, blue tit, marsh tit, willow tit, long-tailed tit) and a few wetland species (snipe, curlew, redshank) which can be found on the farmland but, apart from acknowledging their presence, it is better that these species be left to the chapters on their main habitat.

Also, out of the breeding season, the fields are a feeding area for golden plover, black-headed gull, fieldfare, redwing and others which are dealt with more fully in other parts of the book.

Naturally, it cannot be said that all the breeding species can be found on any one farm, nor for that matter can they all be found on every hundred acres. A farm with a stream lined by aquatic plants, willows and other trees will carry more species and more birds than one without a waterway. Similarly, a mixed farm of grassland for sheep and cattle, with tall sheltering hedgerows and with potatoes or roots as well as corn, will be a better place for birds than one strictly confined to arable. 'Prairie-farming' areas and mono-culture farms will be low on the list of suitability for birds. Altitude can also have an effect on numbers, as also will thin soils (study the density of the rook, page 30) and, in the north at Everton and Misterton, the field divisions are dykes where sedge warbler and reed bunting are prominent members of the farmland community and the regulars are much less numerous.

The statement that our farmland birdlife has not altered very much, must, of course, be qualified by pointing out that there have been some important individual alterations. A 19th-century farmer or naturalist, if he could be brought back, would ask about the disappearance of the corncrake or would be interested in the presence of the turtle dove and collared dove. Whitaker himself would be delighted to hear the skirling song of the breeding curlews. Generally speaking, however, the naturalist of other times would see familiar species and would feel at home.

Four farm areas of Nottinghamshire have been studied in connection with the Common Bird Census organised by the British Trust for Ornithology. Fortunately they were in different localities, thereby providing a guide to the preference and density of the various farmland species.

  1. One study area, of 200 acres at first, and finally 170 acres, was in the northern part of the Vale of Belvoir on the land of Greenhedge Farm near Scarrington (farmed by Mr R. Walker). Most of the fields were of Keuper Marl with three fields of gravel and one of poor ironstone. The survey included permanent pasture used by sheep and cattle (seven fields), hay (one or two fields), corn (two or three fields) and sugar beet (one field), according to variations in cropping.

The first census was carried out in 1963 just after the very severe winter of 1962–3 when casualties in birdlife were considerable, and the figures obtained revealed the farmland population at a low position. The last census, in 1967, followed a period of

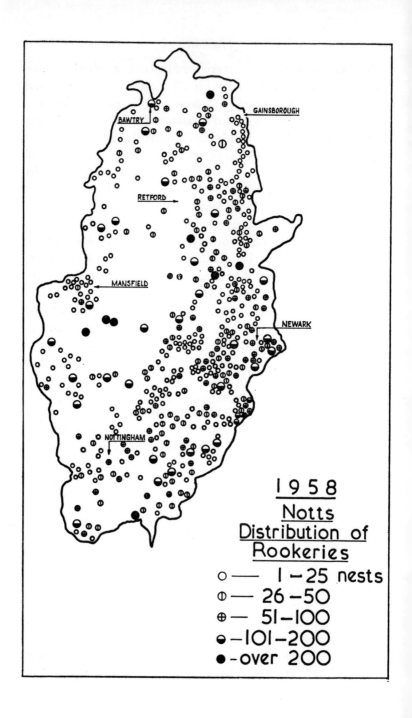

1958
Notts
Distribution of
Rookeries
○ — 1 – 25 nests
◑ — 26 – 50
⊕ — 51 – 100
◖ – 101 – 200
● – over 200

BAWTRY
GAINSBOROUGH
RETFORD
MANSFIELD
NEWARK
NOTTINGHAM

relatively mild winters and the greatly improved species totals, with the exception of the partridge, reflected the recovery of the birds as well as showing the farmland population at a high position. Possibly the average lies in between, and closer to the 1967 position for the resident species.

Results, in pairs of birds (obtained by Mr and Mrs A. Dobbs) were:

	1963 *200 acres*	*1967* *170 acres*
Mallard	—	1
Red-legged partridge	4	1
Common partridge	9	4
Pheasant	—	—
Moorhen	—	Present
Lapwing	—	1
Woodpigeon*	Several + non-breeders	10 + non-breeders
Turtle dove	4	3
Cuckoo	1	1
Skylark	15	22
Swallow	1	1
Carrion crow	—	1
Magpie	1	1
Jay	—	Present
Great tit	1	3
Blue tit	1	3
Marsh tit	—	1
Wren	—	2
Mistle thrush	—	1 probable
Song thrush	2	9
Blackbird	17	31
Robin	2	3
Whitethroat	12	5
Lesser whitethroat	—	Recorded
Spotted flycatcher	—	1
Dunnock	10	17
Yellow wagtail	2–3	1
Starling	3	6 at least
Greenfinch	1	3

* The woodpigeon was subject to control by the farmer and assessment of the population was difficult because of repeat nests.

	1963 200 acres	1967 170 acres
Goldfinch	—	1–2
Linnet	6	13
Bullfinch	—	2
Chaffinch	3	8
Yellowhammer	3	5
Corn bunting	5	4
Reed bunting	—	2
House sparrow†	No count	No count
Tree sparrow	6	4

† The successful house sparrow was, of course, numerous.

2. Another study area was just east of Radcliffe on Trent, where the 180 acres surveyed straddled the parish boundary with Shelford. Beginning at the River Trent the fields rose to the Malkin Hill and, in part, were edged by a strip of woodland. This 180 acres consisted of parts of two arable farms; one rotated barley, beet and tulips, the other wheat and barley. Here there was 30 acres of permanent grassland. This study area was largely arable, ie 83%, and the woodlands gave a touch of variety.

Census results (in pairs) for two years (obtained by Mr J. R. Spencer) were:

	1965 (NB 250 acres)	1968 (NB 180 acres)
Mallard	1	1
Kestrel	—	1
Red-legged partridge	—	2
Common partridge	6	5
Pheasant	3	4
Moorhen	—	1
Lapwing	2	1
Woodpigeon	Numerous. No count	Numerous. No count
Turtle dove	1	1
Collared dove	—	2
Cuckoo	1	1
Tawny owl	—	— Present 1966
Green woodpecker	—	Present

32

Page 33 *(above)* Shelduck; *(below)* black-headed gull with chicks

Page 34
(*above*) Barn owl;
(*left*) little owl

	1965 (*NB 250 acres*)	1968 (*NB 180 acres*)
Skylark	43	32
Sand martin	1	2 Influence of R Trent
Great tit	2	2
Blue tit	17	17
Marsh tit	—	Present
Treecreeper	1	—
Wren	9	12
Mistle thrush	3	Present
Song thrush	14	17
Blackbird	34	22
Robin	12	12
Blackcap	—	5
Garden warbler	1	—
Whitethroat	5	9
Willow warbler	3	7
Spotted flycatcher	6	1
Dunnock	19	16
Pied wagtail	—	Present
Yellow wagtail	12	9
Starling	Present—no count	Present—no count
Greenfinch	3	3
Goldfinch	—	2
Linnet	18	18
Bullfinch	1	2
Chaffinch	33	16
Corn bunting	—	1
Reed bunting	—	Present
House sparrow	No count	No count
Tree sparrow	1	7

3. The third area examined (farmed and studied in 1961 and 1962 by Mr J. R. Mawer) covered 237 acres on Inkersall Lodge Farm; it proved useful for our scrutiny of farmland birds because it is on the Bunter Sandstone, one of the dry areas of Nottinghamshire.

The study area consisted of 220 acres of arable land and the crops basically were barley and sugar beet, with potatoes, kale and swedes at times. The fields, sandy and stony, were described as the 'blow-away type' under drought and windy conditions. Of the hedgerows a few were tall and thick, but most were trimmed and sparse.

A stream of sorts, the Rainworth Water, runs through the property but it became debased first by loss of water due to too much extraction and then, when flow was improved, it was polluted by sewage and coal waste. Recent moves to improve our waterways have seen development which may, in time, see this water clean again. Inkersall Lodge Farm is surrounded by woodland, especially conifer plantations, to the north and west but is open to other farmland to the east.

Average numbers for the species using this census area (including the woodland species using the 11 acres of woodland) were (in pairs):

Mallard	1 at times	Blackbird	6
Red-legged partridge	1–2	Robin	5–6
Common partridge	4–5	Whitethroat	1
Pheasant	3–4	Lesser whitethroat	4–5
Moorhen	1–2	Willow warbler	5–6
Stockdove	1–2	Chiffchaff	1–2
Turtle dove	1	Spotted flycatcher	1
Collared dove	0–1	Dunnock	11
Woodpigeon	2–3	Tree pipit	1–2
Cuckoo	1	Pied wagtail	1–2
Skylark	15	Starling	7
Swallow	8	Greenfinch	4–5
Carrion crow	1	Goldfinch	1
Magpie	2–3	Linnet	4–5
Great tit	2–3	Chaffinch	18–20
Blue tit	2–3	Yellowhammer	10–12
Long-tailed tit	1–2	Corn bunting	3–4
Wren	3–4	Reed bunting	1
Mistle thrush	3	House sparrow	18
Song thrush	3	Tree sparrow	9

4. The fourth census area offered a complete contrast, as it was on part of the highest land in Nottinghamshire close to the 600 foot contour near Wild Hill in the Teversal area. The soil belongs to the Coal Measures, varying from small areas of light gravelly soil through fertile loams to cold, heavy, wet clay.

Mr W. S. Jacklin, another farmer-ornithologist of the Trent Valley Bird Watchers, described his farm and the immediate region as follows: crops were roughly half grass and half arable with permanent grass on the heavier soils. Wheat, oats, barley and a gradually shrinking area of root crops were grown on the more fertile soils.

Hedgerow clearance had not been excessive because the higher rainfall and uneven contours resulted in small streams along the hedgerows, making removal more difficult. The hedges were very varied, but most of them were regularly trimmed and they provided good cover for birds. On some of the opencast restored sites the original hedges had been replaced by post and rail fences with practically no cover for birds.

Because of the high ground the climate is bleak and, combined with the coldness of the soils, snow lies for long periods in winter and early spring. Crops are at least a week later than on the limestone soils only a mile away. This bleakness had probably influenced the continuation of the small field sizes, an average of 10–15 acres.

Census work by Mr Jacklin revealed the following average for 200 acres (in pairs):

Kestrel	Uses the area	Robin	6
Red-legged patridge	1	Mistle thrush	2
Common partridge	4	Song thrush	5
Pheasant	1	Blackbird	16
Lapwing	4	Sedge warbler	1
Turtle dove	1	Blackcap	1
Woodpigeon	5	Whitethroat	7
Cuckoo	Uses the area	Willow warbler	5
Little owl	1	Dunnock	15
Tawny owl	Uses the area	Pied wagtail	1
Skylark	22	Starling	5
Swallow	5	Greenfinch	6
Carrion crow	1	Linnet	9
Magpie	2	Chaffinch	4
Great tit	1	Yellowhammer	9
Blue tit	2	Reed bunting	1
Willow tit	1	Tree sparrow	5
Wren	4	House sparrow	Numerous

To take the totals of the previous four study areas as fully representative of the whole of the Nottinghamshire farmland would be wrong, because of the small sample involved. For instance, for the four study areas, the blackbird lies second to the skylark in numbers, mainly because of the small blackbird population on the sandy Inkersall Lodge Farm; in fact it is reasonably safe to state that on the county's farmland as a whole, the blackbird would be the most numerous species. However, small sample as it is, the figures do give a good idea of the holding capacity of the county's farms, and the fact that the majority of the species found on a farm are of woodland origin may come as a surprise.

A league-table for Nottinghamshire based on density would be similar to the following:

> Blackbird
> Skylark
> Dunnock
> House sparrow—but no figures to support this
> (Linnet, robin, chaffinch, whitethroat—pre-1969, woodpigeon)
> (Song thrush, starling, tree sparrow, yellowhammer)
> Greenfinch
> (Wren, blue tit)

Those bracketed are considered to be about equal numerically. The rest of the species found on farmland would hold only a minor position.

WOODLAND SPECIES

In the ecology of Nottinghamshire, farmland and woodland habitats often merge or are inter-related, and at times, affect each other.

Mention was made of the numbers of woodland species which breed on farmland, and these birds can be divided into species which use a woodland habitat among the fields, those which are able to live fully as farmland/hedgerow species, and some which prefer woodland but spread on to farmland as a secondary habitat at times of peak numbers.

The local woodland today is shown on the map (page 40).

Some 8,000 years ago the amelioration of Britain's climate must have seen a form of cold forest, presumably birch and pine, present in Nottinghamshire and other areas of England. This type of woodland habitat in turn gave way to the deciduous forest when the average temperature stabilised at a higher level, and Nottinghamshire was part of this oak forest, probably from 4,000 BC. This oak type of high forest, plus other hardwoods of course, is still the climax vegetation.

The clearing of the forest to create farmland has been mentioned in the preceding chapter; the present distribution of woodland owes its origins to soil and to English history. On the Bunter Sandstone formation the poor, hungry soil did not attract many early settlers, British, Roman or Saxon, and with the coming of the Norman rulers so keen on the joys of the chase, the still primitive forest of oak and birch with bracken ground-cover stretching northwards for some 20 miles from Nottingham, presented itself as a Royal hunting forest, a sort of medieval conservation area.

For some reason the equally arid heathland north to Yorkshire was not included in the now famous Sherwood Forest. A survey of the forest in 1609 gave an area of 95,000 acres which included

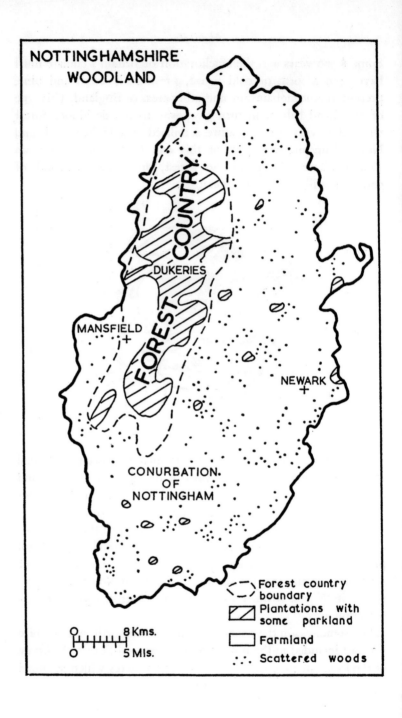

NOTTINGHAMSHIRE WOODLAND

FOREST COUNTRY

DUKERIES

MANSFIELD +

NEWARK +

CONURBATION.
OF
NOTTINGHAM

8 Kms.
5 Mls.

Forest country boundary
Plantations with some parkland
Farmland
Scattered woods

woods, parks, enclosures and water. From this time onwards the high forest became sadly depleted. Many fringe areas, once owned by religious orders, passed into the hands of private landowners from the Dissolution onwards, and in time saw the growth of great estates: mansions, parks and much mixed treeplanting evolved into the area known as the Dukeries. This alteration of the wild oak country of Sherwood may appear a sad thing but the variety of habitats created by the dukes increased the number of bird species.

Following World War I, when further inroads were made upon the woodlands old and new of the sandstone area, there followed more planting by private landowners, and from 1925 the Forestry Commission planted up a considerable acreage. Sherwood Forest lives again, but with acres of conifers instead of sturdy oaks; and its southern boundary is no longer against the walls of Nottingham Castle but a little way beyond the limits of the urban conurbation from Arnold. Furthermore, it stretches further north than the old Sherwood. The map clearly shows the modern 'Forest' area of Nottinghamshire following the sandstone more or less to the Yorkshire border.

To the east of the Forest country lies a huge farmland area, which has been so for centuries. However, the map shows that the marls and clays carry considerable acreage of woodland habitat in the form of small woods, woody parkland, and the escarpment-edge type of woodland. The sandlands of the border with Lincolnshire were planted with conifers at Wigsley and near Coddington, as were the heavier soils on the Cotgrave Wolds, but the rest remained largely valuable deciduous woodland, the home of many species of birds. Recent years have seen a change of habitat here, with conifers replacing the hardwoods, and the established order of our woodland species in these areas begins to alter. As it is said some of this land has been under deciduous trees since the end of the cold forest, it is a pity to see the old ecology destroyed so extensively. Fortunately some woods have been undersown with hardwoods.

Losses have occurred from woodland being converted into

farmland, although this is still minor in significance, and as the purchase of land for new forestry development has now ceased, the acreage of forest and woodland in Nottinghamshire is not likely to exceed 40,000 acres for some time to come. Amenity planting by the County Council including the afforestation of some of the pit tips and derelict ex-quarry land could provide further acreage.

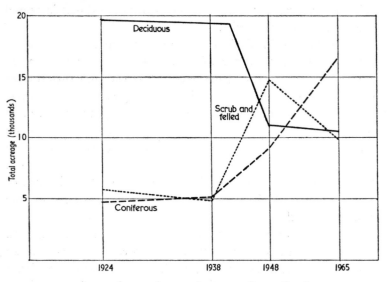

Approximate changes in types of woodland

The breakdown of the main acreage figures for the census years differ from each other, because the sensitivity of the assessment was different and also because the 1965 census did not give mixed high forest, but apportioned it to either predominantly coniferous or predominantly broadleaved high forest. In order to make a graph of broad trends the various acreages have been totalled as either deciduous or coniferous. The mixed high forest has been classed as deciduous, and therefore the figures are approximate only.

This manipulation does not alter the findings very much, and the graph shows the decrease in deciduous, the felling during

World War II, and the post-war surge in coniferous. At the time of writing the trend continues, with coniferous acreage increasing at the expense of scrub and deciduous.

The breeding species of the woodland community which can be expected in Nottinghamshire are pheasant, woodcock, stock dove, woodpigeon, little owl, tawny owl, great spotted woodpecker, jackdaw, jay, great tit, blue tit, coal tit, marsh tit, long-tailed tit, treecreeper, wren, song thrush, blackbird, robin, blackcap, willow warbler, chiffchaff, goldcrest, spotted flycatcher, dunnock, bullfinch, chaffinch.

Some of local or limited distribution are sparrowhawk, collared dove, long-eared owl, nightjar, green woodpecker, lesser spotted woodpecker, willow tit, nuthatch, redstart, nightingale, garden warbler, hawfinch, redpoll.

Just as some woodland species can be found living successfully on farmland, so can field species be found using woodland for breeding purposes; these commute to and from the farmland food supply to the nest—eg kestrel, carrion crow, rook, magpie, mistle thrush, starling, greenfinch, goldfinch, linnet and tree sparrow. Heron (the exception) commutes from water to nest.

Birds of the woodland fringe or the woody heathland must be mentioned, and include whinchat, grasshopper warbler, whitethroat, lesser whitethroat, tree pipit, yellowhammer. The woodlark should be featured here too but, at the time of writing, it seems to have disappeared from Nottinghamshire.

A few species are too rare or breed too spasmodically to be discussed as general members of the county's woodland community and such (Montagu's harrier, wood warbler and crossbill for example) are better left to the Systematic List.

Finally, the list of woodland species is further increased by winter species which feed on or roost in this habitat, including fieldfare, redwing, great grey shrike, siskin and brambling.

Just as one area of farmland can hold more species and more birds than another, according to the variety of habitats, crops, and animals, so can one type of woodland be better for birds than another. The situation is complex because of the ever-changing conditions, as woodland develops from tiny seedlings through the various phases to high forest, with or without drastic alterations by man. It also depends on whether an area of woodland is in a wet or dry situation and, of course, birds are influenced by the type of tree or trees planted.

Prairie-type monoculture was mentioned as the worst farmland habitat for birds, and its woodland counterpart would be the conifer plantation, say of Norway spruce, lacking any deciduous tree or shrub, and draughty at ground level; beech is as a deciduous example. Fortunately these plantations are not too common in Nottinghamshire, because the Forestry Commission have travelled a long way from the original concept of the tree factory. Some twenty or so years ago a member of the Forestry Commission gave a talk on the development of softwoods to the Trent Valley Bird Watchers, and when asked about the Commission's attitude to birdlife loftily replied that the Forestry Commission were there to grow trees, and birds were irrelevant to the process. A decade or so later these trees, bereft of birds, suffered a severe attack of the pine looper moth and a costly spraying process by aeroplane had to be undertaken. Public opinion, too, opposes the dense, dark conifers, and a thin strip of deciduous woodland, often of birch or sycamore, is now used to soften the harsh impact of a new plantation. Very quickly, this simple innovation brought in more species of birds.

The ideal for woodland birds is mixed high forest, where the forester is not tidily active and the variety of trees, the existence of old trees with nesting-holes or crannies, and the presence of a good mixed ground-cover create a living area in any season.

In a conifer plantation, the feature which strikes the birdwatcher is the almost complete silence. The density of birds per acre is very small and a Nottinghamshire plantation would hold a few coal tits, a robin or two, an occasional tree creeper, a furtive jay which would be heard rather than seen, and of course some woodpigeons. If the area was a good one for voles a long-eared

owl might be discovered. However, now that forestry has been
carried out commercially for some forty-six years on a large scale,
it would not be fair to give this as the sole picture of our county's
softwood habitat. Active forestry creates a series of habitats and,
after an area has been clear-felled, the stages from replanting are:

Stage 1	*Tree Stage*	*Birds*
0–5 years	Young trees and growth of low 'weeds' —heather, gorse, bramble, grasses	Whinchat, lapwing—very early stage, nightjar (sandy soil), skylark initially, meadow pipit?, tree pipit, blackbird, some warblers—eg grasshopper warbler, whitethroat, willow warbler, yellowhammer, linnet, reed bunting
Stage 2		
5–15 years	Thicket stage. Dense growth of trees and weeds species (depending on site), eg birch, sallow, thorn, briar, bramble. Conifer and/or deciduous trees at scrub size	The period of highest bird population, especially as regards density per acre. Whinchat, grasshopper warbler, tree pipit and other open-area species would decline to be replaced by robin, wren, willow warbler, blackcap, garden warbler, redpoll, chaffinch, turtle dove, etc
Stage 3		
15–30 years	The pole stage, when trees are dominant and the closed canopy kills off other vegetation and also the lower branches of the trees	Top-canopy species only, eg chiffchaff, wood warbler, goldcrest, redpoll. Low-canopy and shrub species around edges, especially if conifers encircled by deciduous screen. A general decrease in bird numbers, but tits usually widespread, and owls, jay and woodpigeon 'comfortable'

| 30 years to rotation end | Tall trees with some ground vegetation. Trees dominant | *Beech stand*—high-canopy species only. Little or no ground vegetation. *Ash, oak, sycamore*—canopy species and some shrub species. *Conifer, spruce*—canopy species only. *Pine*—canopy species and a few shrub species. *Larch*—canopy species and a moderate number of shrub species. (Allows thick bramble growth on heavy soils.) Willow warbler, chiffchaff, chaffinch, blackcap, redstart (light soil), tit species |
| over-mature | Dead and dying trees. Opening of the canopy. Tree dominance declining. Increase of shrubs | Canopy species plus increase in numbers of shrub species |

All these stages will exist at the same time somewhere in the forest area, and the number of species and their density will rise and fall according to the habitat stage. There will be a shift of position as each species seeks out and settles into its particular habitat.

A Forestry Commission area was studied (by S. A. Rowlands) for the BTO Common Birds Census, and the results on 50 acres in the Clipstone Forest portray very well the bird wealth possible when a conifer area has deciduous edges, parts underset with hardwood, adjacent farmland and a cleared area. The area was a plantation containing mostly Scots and Corsican pine at varying ages, from 16 to 18 years (40%) to 35 and 50 years old. The rides were lined with hardwoods, mostly sycamore and birch of various ages. A 6-acre area of 16-year-old Scots pine also included an equal amount of beech which, because of its slower growth, formed a shrub layer, and this part held most of the willow warblers.

Although fairly evenly distributed the chaffinch was found

most densely in an area mostly of 50-year-old Scots pine with some Corsican pine and European larch.

Two very wide rides, including a road, contained the spotted flycatcher, the turtle doves and many of the yellowhammers which were probably increased by the farmland on several sides.

The Rowlands' totals for 1965 (in pairs) were:

Chaffinch	27	Coal tit	3
Willow warbler	22	Turtle dove	2
Woodpigeon (not		Great tit	2
counted but		Tree pipit	1
probably	14–20)	Spotted flycatcher	1
Blackbird	13	Jay	1
Yellowhammer	13	Tree sparrow	1
Robin	9	Blue tit	1
Wren	6	Cuckoo	1
Song thrush	6	Magpie	1
Chiffchaff	4	Whitethroat	1
Dunnock	3	Garden warbler	1

Other species recorded but not breeding within the study area were: swallow, swift, starling, blackcap, pheasant, redstart, house martin, bullfinch. For a mainly conifer area, the variety of species for this particular 50 acres is very good, and there are many plantations far less rich. It is worth noting that the tree pipit occurred in a small area which had been burnt and was regenerating.

J. R. Spencer has carried out a Common Bird Census in 45 acres of woodland at Rufford, where silver birch is dominant with yew, oak, sycamore, rowan and a few conifers adding variety. The soil is sandy, being on the Bunter, and therefore bracken is part of the ground-cover. Some bramble, nettles, honeysuckle and willow herb is present, while rhododendrons provide denser cover.

Mr Spencer's figures show the recovery from the severe 1962–3 winter very well and his 1968 results, after five mild winters, probably represent this particular population at a high level.

His totals (in pairs) were:

Robin	29	Tree sparrow	4
Wren	29	Collared dove	3
Dunnock	27	Jay	3
Blue tit	24	Long-tailed tit	2
Willow warbler	21	Mistle thrush	2
Chaffinch	15	Whitethroat	2
Blackbird	11	Tree pipit	2
Great tit	10	Yellowhammer	2
Blackcap	9	Treecreeper	1
Song thrush	6	Redstart	1
Coal tit	4	Goldcrest	1
Marsh tit	4	Spotted flycatcher	1
Chiffchaff	4	Woodpigeon	(Not
Bullfinch	4		counted)

Species which have bred in previous years, but were not proved to breed in 1968 were: woodcock, nuthatch, cuckoo, willow tit, starling, magpie. Other species present at times, but not proved to breed, were: garden warbler, great spotted woodpecker, lesser whitethroat, hawfinch, lesser redpoll.

The blackbird is rather low down in the list, probably because of the dry conditions and low earthworm population, and also because of a shortage in suitable nest sites. With the growth of the silver birch the reduction in the amount of open space caused the yellowhammer to decrease from five pairs to two in three years.

The two survey areas show what types of woodland may hold and how one wood can differ considerably from another. If, however, we lift our eyes from the immediate surroundings and take in this heartland of Nottinghamshire's forest country, from Clipstone Forest and Thieves Wood in the south to the outskirts of Worksop and Apley Head in the north, we see some 80 square miles (207 square kilometres) of varied habitats holding considerable numbers of many species, the stronghold for a number of them. Here are represented all types of woodland from, birdwise, the worst example of conifer plantation to the best, from the oak forest to the parkland woods of many species of trees; and on the whole the result is very satisfying for the ornithologist.

Pilgrimage to the Major Oak never slackens, in fact the pressure of human feet in this area increases annually as more and more foreign visitors join the throng. At the time of writing there are moves to create this remnant of Old Sherwood as a conservation area with the replanting of oaks to replace those ravaged by time, air pollution, and desert conditions. This will also be for the good of the rich birdlife which the findings of the TVBW have proved to exist there. Close by are the estates of Thoresby, Welbeck, Clumber and Osberton where the student of trees can spend hours on the many varieties of deciduous and coniferous. Pleasing too, is the present new feeling for trees, for hardwoods in an amenity sense, which will offset, to some extent, the planting of softwoods on the commercial side of forestry.

Here in this forest heartland, in the old oaks or among the mature hardwoods, the redstart and the nuthatch are in numbers; the searcher will find the lesser spotted woodpecker, whereas elsewhere he may or may not; the hawfinch is here, attached at certain times of the year to the hornbeams; and when the green woodpecker was killed by severe cold in other woodland areas, here in Old Sherwood and the Dukeries it survived to start the recolonisation of lost ground. Until its remarkable increase, the lesser redpoll was almost confined to this forest stronghold, and in winter it was and still is joined by wandering flocks of Continental and northern redpolls feasting upon the birch seed; while in the wetter places where the alders grow, siskins come every autumn for the seed. Significantly, the last proof of breeding crossbills was in this area where, as the summer dusk falls and the last of the car trippers move off, the woodcock and the nightjar take over.

King Pheasant and Lord Partridge are still accorded too much authority here but, apart from a sad relapse now and then when a shot kestrel or owl is found, the rearing of the game birds is more enlightened and the sparrowhawk, kestrel and others of the hooked beak are given their chance to fit into the forest community. Some of the keepers have proved to be quite knowledgeable on conservation, in keeping with the present-day outlook, and are probably the forerunners of a new type of gamekeeper.

Public desire to enjoy the amenities of parkland and forest can have an adverse effect. The heron quickly deserted Clumber once it was open to the public, finding sanctuary in the private woodlands of Welbeck and Osberton. The birdwatcher knows that quiet areas are necessary to act as reservoirs to preserve plants, trees, animals, birds and insects. He sees a private heath, for instance, holding tree pipit, whinchat, skylark and other species of the open areas; but once allow in the motor-car family, the ball players, and the roaming pet dog, and he sees the area almost dead as far as these breeding birds are concerned.

No specific surveys of any particular area of the Keuper Marl woodland have been carried out by members of the TVBW. These deciduous woods hold a typical community of woodland species with the blackbird and song thrush in greater numbers than on the dry sandstone. The blackcap too, is very much at home and certain woods have long been the traditional breeding sites for most of our few nightingales. Naturally the bird species differ in number and kind according to the type of tree or trees and to the kind of undergrowth. Certain species are missing or extremely local. The mixed deciduous woodland general some thirty years ago is being altered radically with the introduction of coniferous species. It will lead to some impoverishment of the bird species and could affect the numbers of nightingales and marsh tits unless there is a mixture of hard and softwood trees or conservation plans allow for the provision of cover.

Woodlands on the Lias and Boulder Clay have also been converted to conifer and the process continues, with the result that, in some cases, deciduous woodland of ancient lineage is being lost. If economics dictate that coniferous trees are a must, then conservation methods are also a 'must', and should take the form of planting deciduous fringes and deciduous corners where rides meet, and providing undergrowth to ensure homely conditions for wildlife. The day of the conifer factory in laboratory-type plantations is over.

Two small areas which cover the escarpment type of deciduous woodland, as found along the edges of the Trent Valley (at

(*right*) Great spotted
woodpecker;

(*below*) great tit

Page 52 (*above*) Swallow with young; (*below*) song thrush and young

Clifton, Radcliffe, Burton Joyce, Flintham etc) and also along the steep slopes of the Dumbles where streams have made small ravines in the Keuper (Lambley, Epperstone, Halloughton, etc) were surveyed.

The ¾ mile stretch below Clifton Hall, of about 23 acres, was studied from 1956 to 1958 when it was still private property. It was found to hold (in pairs):

Robin	9	Marsh tit	1–2
Blackbird	8	Long-tailed tit	1
Wren	6	Lesser spotted woodpecker	1
Chaffinch	6–8	Green woodpecker	1
Willow warbler	5	Great spotted woodpecker	1
Blue tit	4	Mistle thrush	1
Blackcap	4	Nuthatch	1
Song thrush	3–4	Chiffchaff	1
Jackdaw	3–4	Whitethroat	1
Dunnock	2	Spotted flycatcher	1
Great tit	2	Greenfinch	1
Starling	2	Stockdove	1
Woodpigeon	2		

Carrion crow, magpie, jay, cuckoo, goldcrest and kestrel were present occasionally but breeding was not proved. Willow tit was recorded once.

The woodland was mainly deciduous, including horse chestnut, lime, beech, elm, willow and alder. There was a stand of 48 sparse conifers and much elder scrub.

A survey of Trent Valley edge-woodland in the form of a derelict garden was carried out at Gedling House for the School Museum Service. The grounds were of 8 acres containing a mixture of beech, yew, oak, lime, birch, etc. The results (in pairs) were:

Blackbird	9	Great tit	2
Song thrush	7	Willow warbler	2
Starling	7	Chiffchaff	3
Robin	5	Tree sparrow	1–2
Wren	5	Carrion crow	1
Dunnock	5	Jackdaw	1

D

Woodpigeon	Several	Jay	1
Chaffinch	4	Mistle thrush	1
Spotted flycatcher	4	Blackcap	1
Greenfinch	3	Whitethroat	1
Blue tit	2	Bullfinch	1

Cuckoo, tawny owl, magpie, coal tit, marsh tit, treecreeper and linnet were present, and the house and outbuildings provided homes for 4 pairs of swallows and numerous house sparrows. The dominance of blackbird and song thrush was due to the garden hedgerow bordering extensive playing fields, ideal feeding areas for these two species.

Finally a closer look at the hierarchy of the woodland bird community is necessary. A table on density in woodland, to compare with the farmland findings, would be in roughly this order:

Robin
(Blue tit, wren)
Willow warbler
Blackbird
(Chaffinch, dunnock)
(Great tit, song thrush, woodpigeon)
Starling

On a fine, warm day in late March, the territorial songs of the many robins is a striking feature; early spring is probably the only time when the true dominant position of this bird can be realised without a careful census. On moist land the blackbird will, it is thought, outnumber the robin in some woodland habitats, but in general remembering our areas of light, dry soils, the blackbird's position is considered to be around the fourth most numerous in this habitat.

Of the remaining woodland species most occupy a minor position numerically although, in the normal run of things, chiffchaff, blackcap and whitethroat are always obvious, while coal tit, jay, yellowhammer, tree sparrow, linnet and greenfinch show up well in certain types of woodland habitat.

WETLAND SPECIES

Nottinghamshire is a well-watered county, almost all of it drained by the River Trent system, the exceptions being a small stream north-west of Sutton-in-Ashfield and sundry little streams which flow into Lincolnshire east of Newark. The domination of the River Trent is fully shown on the map of surface drainage (page 56), as is the dry area of the Bunter Sandstone. The Maun, Meden and Poulter, feeders of the River Idle, appear to be a source of major drainage but, because they pass through the porous sandstone, the volume of water carried is unexpectedly small and not in keeping with the system.

Within this complex drainage system there are natural streams, man-made dykes, pools, lakes, reservoirs and gravel pits, a diversity of habitat to support those bird species associated with watery or marshy conditions. Unfortunately, in these days of excessive pollution, a map of rivers and streams does not portray an identical quality of habitat. Ornithologically, the rivers and streams of Nottinghamshire are for the most part, wholesome

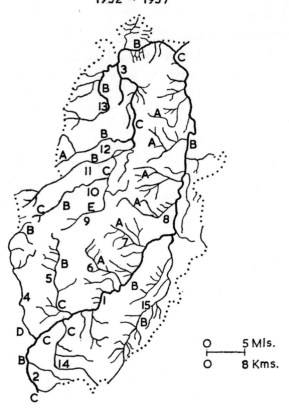

NOTTINGHAMSHIRE GRADED SURFACE DRAINAGE
1952 – 1957

1. R. Trent	9. Rainworth Water
2. R. Soar	10. R. Maun
3. R. Idle	11. R. Meden
4. R. Erewash	12. R. Poulter
5. R. Leen	13. R. Ryton
6. Dover Beck	14. Fairham Brook
7. R. Greet	15. R. Smite
8. The Beck	

The grades used by the Trent River Board shown on the above map are as follows:

A   Pure enough for trout and grayling, and for caddis and mayflies.

B   Clean enough for chub, dace, roach and water shrimps.

C   Suitable for roach and gudgeon, and for loglice and leeches.

D   Strongly polluted. No fish, but bloodworms.

E   Barren. Heavily polluted. Some fungus and tubifex worms in places.

habitats but, just as the quality of the water varies in the various stretches, so does the habitat. This is due to the destruction of the natural watercourses and the creation of uninteresting dykes where the banks have been straightened and smoothed, and where barbed wire has replaced the streamside trees, bushes and coarse vegetation. It is a debased habitat for birdlife as can be witnessed along such streams as the River Smite, the Car Dyke and parts of the Fairham Brook. Such drainage is probably very good farming practice, but it has left nowhere for the sedge warbler, reed bunting and kingfisher to nest.

All our streams are feeders for the various lakes, and naturally, the quality of water entering determines the bird ecology of these waters. None of these are isolated bird habitats; they form zones and the birdlife is better appreciated when studied in a zonal context.

Beginning in the north, *Zone 1* is the whole of the county from the Yorkshire border to a line from Worksop to North Leverton. This zone has lacked long-established lakes, apart from the small waters at Langold and Carlton in Lindrick which have played an extremely minor role in providing habitat for wildfowl. Large sheets of water were eventually provided by the extraction of sand and gravel, when flooded gravel pits at Finningley, Blaxton, Misson, Lound, Torworth and Mattersey, especially from 1945 onwards, considerably enhanced this area for the ornithologist. The pits have closely followed the Trent Valley gravel-pit network in providing continued interest and, unfortunately, the ultimate demise of some areas from drainage, and from filling by tipping, with fly ash to come.

This zone held a considerable acreage of water meadow in the valleys of the Rivers Ryton and Idle where redshank, snipe, lapwing and curlew found favourable breeding grounds. This type of wetland has disappeared rapidly since the change in farming from stock to arable, bringing drainage schemes rapidly carried out with earth-moving machines. There are still some tussocky, marshy meadows, but each year their number grows less.

On the credit side in this assessment of wetland has been the accidental creation of floodland which is perhaps the ideal habitat for so many birds liking water. Disrupted land drainage was the cause, during the 1960s perhaps due to subsidence. Flooded areas in the Idle Valley have attracted a wealth of wildfowl, including large numbers of Bewick's swan, wigeon and teal. A large concentration, say 100 Bewick's swan, 600 wigeon and 500 teal, if disturbed by indiscriminate shooters tend to scatter throughout the zone in a number of smaller groups.

Finally, mention must be made of the Carrlands, a flat, low-lying area only some 5–15 feet above sea level. A complicated network of channels gradually evolved in order to lift and move the water away, and this is an area where ditches and dykes take the place of the hedgerow as field boundaries and, consequently, where sedge warbler (even reed warbler in places) and reed bunting are familiar farmland species, instead of blackbird, robin and dunnock. Such an extent of water courses must attract many interesting species, especially in migration periods, but the area is not well covered by observers, although, as could be expected, the Carrlands have provided some bittern records.

Zone 2, known as the Dukeries, begins from Worksop and Retford in the north, includes Welbeck, Carburton and Clumber Park, and ends on a line from Clipstone and Rufford to near Weston in the east. By building dams across the streams the various dukes created a miniature lakeland and, naturally, a wonderful area for aquatic species in a dry sandstone region. The major waters are Welbeck Great Lake (89 acres), Carburton Upper and Lower Dams (40 acres), Clumber Lake (83 acres), Thoresby Lake (60 acres) and Rufford Lake (25 acres).

Both Sterland and Whitaker described the importance of these lakes for wildfowl and Whitaker wrote: 'amongst our other wild fowl, this Duck (the Mallard) is found in greatest numbers, and hundreds congregate on the big lakes at Welbeck, Rufford, Clumber, Newstead and Thoresby.' This happy state of affairs has continued down to present times, as the totals made by members of the Trent Valley Bird Watchers on winter wildfowl counts fully testify.

Flighting from one Dukeries water to another is regular according to the amount of disturbance and, as previously stated, assessment is only possible by making these waters one unit. However, changes have taken place during the last twenty years, partly due to changes in use, possibly also to silting up, and obviously in some cases to mining subsidence. In the 1950s Welbeck was the best water, often carrying at peak times 1,000–1,200 birds (700–900 mallard, 80–200 pochard, and smaller groups of tufted duck, goosander and goldeneye) whereas, by 1970, peak numbers were a good 50% down, perhaps due to increased fishing activity. Clumber, when released by the Army, held very few ducks which, because of the narrowness of this lake, were quickly up and away. Now the lake is used extensively as a rest and preen sanctuary, especially by mallard, which have topped the 1,000 total more than once. Thoresby has been consistently good, although loss of the upper reaches to silt may be the reason for a big reduction in teal. Mallard too are sometimes a little down, due possibly to disturbance by fishermen. The Carburton Dams have always shown variable numbers for the same reason. Rufford, the last of these Dukeries waters, was a good wildfowl water in Whitaker's day, but suffered considerably from pollution by sewage effluent and then by coal silt from colliery washings. During the early years of the wildfowl counts the numbers of birds here were low. Advice was given by the TVBW on ways of bringing in wildfowl, and by 1964, it was used by 200 or more mallard as a rest area. In the late 1960s mining subsidence ruined the lake to such an extent that the Nottinghamshire County Council have been forced to undertake extensive work to bring it to life again. Other smaller waters in the Worksop area have been similarly affected.

A typical winter count result (1969–70 period, following a succession of mild winters) for December or January would give similar results to the following:

	Welbeck	Carburton Dams	Clumber	Thoresby	Rufford	Total
Mallard	300	110	670	650	50	1,780
Teal	40	—	—	90	—	130
Wigeon	—	—	—	—	—	—

	Welbeck	Carburton Dams	Clumber	Thoresby	Rufford	Tota
Shoveler	5	1	—	—	—	6
Tufted duck	76	190	160	20	—	446
Pochard	185	—	6	14	—	205
Goosander	5	—	—	14	—	19
Canada goose	250	—	80	—	30	360
Goldeneye	1	—	1	2	—	4
Mute swan	4	—	30	8	—	42

Other species occur from time to time, such as the gadwall, which is regular in very small numbers, and pintail, scaup, smew, merganser, shelduck, whooper swan and Bewick's swan.

Wigeon do not frequent the Dukeries waters and it is almost an event to record one or two birds, whereas Whitaker spoke of 'goodly numbers' in his day. Tufted duck have shown a considerable increase from an average peak of 100 in the 1950s to over four times that in about fifteen years. This could be due to the long run of mild winters, because coot have increased from a mere 50 or so to 1,800 in the same period. Goosander have become reduced from a regular wintering group of 50, sometimes 80, to an average of less than 20 with occasional peaks of 30–40.

During the breeding season, broods of mallard, tufted duck and Canada goose are a familiar sight. This area provided the first successful breeding for gadwall within the county in 1968. With so much shore-line and fish-bearing water of both stream and lake, other species such as little grebe, great crested grebe, moorhen, kingfisher, reed bunting and waterside warblers are very much part of the habitat and the heron maintains itself, thanks to the protection and peace of the private estates. In the marshy recesses of rush, sedge and willow the water rail winters and, at times, a pair have been proved to breed.

Just to the south of the Dukeries lies *Zone 3*, Central Nottinghamshire, which is partly connected to the Dukeries by the flights of mallard and Canada geese but, also, is linked with the Trent Valley. It is a large area with scattered, usually small, waters of which the Mansfield (King's Mill) Reservoir (70 acres), the Moorgreen Reservoir (44 acres) and the Newstead Abbey Lakes (22 and 13 acres respectively) are the most important.

The extensive (for Nottinghamshire) King's Mill Reservoir was always attractive to water species and was frequently mentioned by Whitaker. It lost this quality when local schools made it a centre for sailing and now only small numbers of wildfowl are present when the sailing boats are moored. It is probably heavily polluted.

Man's activities have affected the Moorgreen Reservoir too, by mining subsidence, which during the TVBW years of recording has reduced this water to a mere trickle on at least two occasions. Since 1964 it has been full enough again to be a useful wildfowl resort, carrying 300–400 mallard at peak times, sometimes more, and often up to 400 teal, so it is an important water for this species. Other species such as tufted duck and pochard, frequent this reservoir, but numbers are not exceptional.

The ponds of Annesley Park were useful links in the chain of waters and represented a halfway stage, especially for mallard, on the route to Newstead Abbey. The main pond, or small lake, was drained for alterations connected with fishing in 1966 and no reports of wildfowl have been received since. Once restored the duck should return to this area again although, because of the small waters, it is easily disturbed.

The waters of Newstead Abbey play their part in providing suitable habitat, although the area cannot be classed as a major one, being chiefly a winter haunt for 40–60 tufted duck, very variable numbers of mallard which occasionally reach 200, and small groups of pochard and teal. The enclosed nature of these waters with their woodland surroundings make the mallard nervous, and the tendency for the waters to freeze over quickly during frosty weather also limits their holding power. Oxton Bogs, Kirklington Lake and mill pond and Ossington Lake occasionally hold good flocks of mallard, up to 200, but for the main part they are minor waters, along with a few other places such as Bulwell Hall.

Other species attracted to this zone's watery places include great crested grebe, little grebe, Canada goose, kingfisher, snipe, etc, while the reed warbler breeds here and there, and the sedge warbler and reed bunting almost everywhere. All these waters, from the large King's Mill Reservoir to the smaller ponds, play their part in preserving a wetland habitat for plants, insects and birds, and when a water is lost (Papplewick Dam and Salterford Dam for instance) it is a tragedy.

The Trent Valley, *Zone 4*, must have ranked as a great place for water species of birds right down the ages, with marshland annually flooded and replenished. Whitaker mentioned that this beautiful river formed a great attraction for many species of birds, and in his book he names places along the valley where unusual species were frequently observed; but one feels he, himself, did not know the area well, because he never wrote intimately of it as he did of his own forest country. In the times of the Trent Valley Bird Watchers the Nottingham Sewage Farm of some 1,100 acres proved a wonderful area for wildfowl, waders and other species connected with marshy vegetation, and yet Whitaker, viewing the area from a train, wrote only of black-headed gulls. The role of this sewage farm as a great inland marsh began in 1880 and continued until modernisation saw an end to the old-style irrigation (1960–1). Fortunately the numbers and species using the area were well recorded for some twenty years, thereby catching a point in time when the voice of the curlew was heard almost more frequently than the sparrow's! Even after drastic alteration the sewage farm continues to draw interesting birds to wet places created when surplus water has to be put on to a patch of ground. This small echo of the great happenings of the lost era serves to show that the Trent Valley is still an important highway and a place for water-loving birds.

The old-style sewage farm attracted good numbers of wildfowl and 300–400 mallard, 400–500 teal, sometimes 200–300 shoveler and 300 wigeon, were there during the autumn and winter. During the breeding season up to 30 pairs of shoveler bred, plus a number of mallard and teal and, at times, a pair of shelduck. Colonies of black-headed gulls, numerous moorhens, and many sedge warblers, yellow wagtails and reed buntings helped to throng this area, which only lacked frogs and fish to have been an ideal wetland habitat.

Other wet areas, such as the northern end of the Besthorpe Fleet, the low-lying and often flooded willow holts, and the marshes of Wilford and Dunkirk, all supported a varied birdlife until many were drained. To the birdwatcher of the Nottinghamshire Trent Valley the loss of so much wetland would have been traumatic but for the development of the sand and gravel industry, especially during and since World War II, which created a chain of waters from Attenborough in the south-west to Girton, north of Newark. Although the extent of this type of habitat is constantly changing, it must have provided 600–800 acres for at least twenty-five years.

The Attenborough gravel-pit complex, started in 1929, has gone from strength to strength, thanks to the system of water transport, and is the 'Jupiter' of the Trent Valley, due to its size and role as a first-class nature reserve. Others rivalled it closely for a time until infilling reduced their size. Besthorpe gravel pit had a central area of marshy fen, dating from pre-quarrying times, which improved its attractions for waders. But earth and fly-ash filling have almost ended its usefulness as a wetland habitat, and its glory lingers only in the records of the TVBW. Hoveringham followed Besthorpe into decline, due to fly-ash filling and sailing, but its attractiveness is by no means extinguished.

Holme Pierrepont gradually attained a three-star rating which, at times, was marred by over-shooting and water skiing. Now, in its new role as an International Rowing Course and Water Recreation Area, it will continue to attract birds in a more limited way. Netherfield, nicely positioned on the NE-SW flyway, has always attracted tired wanderers. Unfortunately, there was not the scope for extensive development and, once the widest stretch west of the railway had been reduced by tipping, it failed to compete with the other larger areas. However, with further quarry development at nearby Colwick, the combined areas (approx 3 square miles) of Holme Pierrepont, Colwick and Netherfield from the mid-1960s onwards must have had considerable 'pulling power' on migrants needing a rest.

Smaller gravel waters worked at Gunthorpe, Averham, Balderton, South and North Muskham, Cromwell, Winthorpe and Girton have contributed to the wetland habitat and to the ornithology of the Trent Valley, though restricted by fishing, boating and shooting.

The ecology of a gravel-pit complex eventually provides suitable breeding areas for all or some of these: great crested grebe, little grebe, mallard, teal, garganey, shoveler, tufted duck, pochard, Canada goose, mute swan, water rail, moorhen, coot, little ringed plover, black-headed gull, common tern, sand martin, willow tit, reed warbler, sedge warbler, pied wagtail, yellow wagtail, reed bunting and other species associated with a wild, weedy area unconnected with water. Added to the above are the temporary visitors such as the waders on migration, the winter wildfowl, the various gulls, and chance visitors in the shape of marsh harrier, osprey, or even a skua.

No two gravel pit areas are exactly alike: differences occur from the methods of extracting the gravel. Transporting by barge is locally unique to Attenborough; there is the general grab and load, using a crane on caterpillar tracks and big-tyred trucks; there are later refinements such as draining an area for extraction; and finally the 'hills and hollows' sideways method, which makes long, narrow troughs from which the gravel is moved by conveyor belt. The birdlife, as listed above, is basically similar except that one method may provide more suitable habitat for some species than others. For instance, any method which creates a large sheet of open water is good for wildfowl, while the drain and flood region can produce more open ground for the little ringed plover. The use of barges at Attenborough sets up a system of connected water channels which sees more open water and aquatic vegetation for the great crested grebe and sedge warbler, etc. The narrow trough system attracts the least variety of species. Nevertheless, each gravel-pit complex carries a similar 'clientele' and attracts the same migratory species in need of food and rest. What a gravel-pit habitat (always full of fish) mainly lacks are areas of shallow water, open or in cover. One or other of the larger gravel pits, especially where there is a large lagoon, is used as a gull roost.

With the establishing of an electric power-station complex along the River Trent and the consequent infilling of the gravel pits with fly ash, the 'boom and boon' of this type of ornithology seemed doomed. Fortunately, an official awareness that some of these water areas are more valuable as recreational centres than as restored flood-plain pasture or farmland has set in motion plans which will forestall the fly ash here and there, and preserve some water areas for aquatic sports and, both unintentionally and intentionally, for water and waterside birds. The Attenborough Nature Reserve, conceived and developed by local naturalists from the old gravel workings, has played a major role in conserving aquatic species in the Nottingham area.

The advent of power stations led to more bird deaths from collisions with the lines of the vast grid system; but, on the credit side, the temperature of the river water has been raised, so that, when everywhere is in the deadly grip of severe cold, the Trent flows serenely on, warm and genial. It is not surprising that divers, grebes, ducks and, for a time as they move south-westwards, the various waders, congregate on or beside the river.

As in the valley of the River Idle, flooded land, often washland created to take the threat from a flood, attracts water birds and when grassland is under water the numbers of wigeon and teal rise suddenly. These birds, and the flocks of dunlin, probably come into the Trent Valley from the Humber. During the breeding season any such spot, if moist cattle pastures, will be frequented by lapwing, redshank and perhaps snipe, and of course by the yellow wagtail.

A normal peak mid-winter wildfowl count for the whole of the Trent Valley in Nottinghamshire during the years near to 1970 would produce something close to the following: mallard 1,600; teal 750; wigeon 700; shoveler 15; tufted duck 600; pochard 400; goldeneye 15; goosander 10; shelduck 6; Canada goose 20; mute swan 60; Bewick's swan 8. The Attenborough Reserve, an excellent refuge, usually carries from 30%–40% of the Trent Valley peak population.

Mention must be made of the minor city waters (the University

Lake, Martin's Pond and the small ponds of the parks at Vernon Road, Arnot Hill and the Arboretum) which achieve some importance as refuges for mallard during severe wintry weather.

The final area, *Zone 5*, includes South and East Nottinghamshire comprising the course of the River Smite, the Vale of Belvoir, the Wolds and the West Leake Hills, where the streams are slow and small, and the lakes also are of small acreage. The wildfowl of Flintham Hall Lake are really offshoots from the Trent Valley, and usually only small numbers of mallard plus a spring or two of teal frequent the Bunny, Stanford Hall and Kingston Hall waters, plus the few ponds scattered about.

A feature of this zone is the derelict Grantham Canal, formerly an attractive habitat but now, in parts, hardly better than a wide drainage ditch; it only recaptures a little of its original ecology where the presence of water encourages reed and sedge warblers and a muddy fringe pulls in the occasional itinerant snipe or sandpiper. A start has been made on restoring it.

Zone 5 ends at the county boundary marked by the River Soar, where a flood-plain habitat once again provides a home for lapwing, redshank and curlew and a winter feeding area for wildfowl, especially the dabbling species. Most of this suitable ground lies in Leicestershire, and our interest lies in the wildfowl which often flight to Attenborough when disturbed.

BUILT-UP AREA SPECIES

The suburban habitat is an ever-increasing one, and no modern book on the county's ornithology can ignore it, because many birds have developed the ability to live and survive among the detached and semi-detached dwellings which sprawl outwards from the city and town, and also which spring up in mushroom fashion in some country areas.

The conurbation of Nottingham from the city centre to its outer limits at Toton, Stapleford, Bulwell, Arnold, Gedling and Ruddington covers at least 50 square miles and, excluding small areas such as villages, a further 35 square miles can be added for

other build-up zones in the county. In these 85 square miles, in a habitat of privet hedges, lawns, flower beds, allotments, recreation grounds, parks, industrial wasteland, used and unused railway tracks, bungalows, houses, factories and tall blocks of flats, thousands of birds live with the majority of Nottinghamshire's population: about 86% of Nottinghamshire people, about 690,000, live in the suburban–urban habitat, their lives controlled by the availability of employment, homes and such amenities as educational establishments, libraries, theatres and sports grounds.

The Nottingham City area has the largest and most dense zone, with about half a million people living in 50 square miles, and this is joined by an almost continuous stretch of housing to

Derby. Because of rapid growth and a lack of planning, this habitat, although providing essential housing, fails to provide an entirely adequate living area for the human species and, as will be shown, it is also incomplete in some ways for the birds. But, just as the human beings make the best of a poor job, so do the birds!

The breeding species of the built-up habitat in the Nottingham area are:

Kestrel	Blue tit
Stockdove	Coal tit
Woodpigeon	Marsh tit
Feral pigeon	Wren
Collared dove	Mistle thrush
Cuckoo	Song thrush
Little owl	Blackbird
Tawny owl	Robin
Swift	Spotted flycatcher
Swallow	Dunnock
House martin	Starling
Sand martin	Greenfinch
Carrion crow	Goldfinch
Rook	Linnet
Jackdaw	Chaffinch
Magpie	House sparrow
Great tit	

The mallard, mute swan and moorhen also qualify, because these species have actually nested in urban or suburban built-up situations, though only in a limited, isolated way.

The term 'built-up' here is used in a narrow sense and concerns those parts which are covered with housing, in the main, plus the occasional open space. When Greater Suburbia for the Nottingham conurbation is considered and we include the spacious Wollaton Park, the University grounds, industrial wasteland and the half-and-half boundary with open country, more breeding species can be added such as coot, jay, skylark, whitethroat, goldcrest, redstart, treecreeper, willow warbler, chiffchaff, pied wagtail and bullfinch, but such an extension takes us away from the main part of this habitat which is where people live.

Before dealing in more detail with the suburban species, mention must be made of the black redstart, which has bred in the very centre of Nottingham alongside the feral pigeon, the house sparrow and the kestrel.

As in the farmland and the woodland areas some districts offer a greater or better variety of habitat, more garden space for example; for obvious reasons, an outer suburban district will be better than an urban, inner one. The district of Woodthorpe was studied (by A. Dobbs) from 1958 to 1967, and the results of this work will serve to show the bird-holding qualities of the better (from a naturalist's point of view) type of suburb.

Woodthorpe is approximately 4 miles north of the centre of Nottingham and is the southern part of the Arnold Urban District. At the commencement of the study it had considerable open areas comprising some allotments and several rough fields, and it was open to the countryside to the east. Two parks, Woodthorpe Grange to the south and Arnot Hill to the north, which were connected by two disused railway lines, also increased the district's wildlife potential.

Most of the houses in the 380 acres studied were provided with good-sized gardens resulting in the row of houses on one road being separated from the houses on the adjacent road by a long and quite wide (40–60 yards) stretch of 'country', the equivalent to open woodland. Some of the larger houses on the western side, bordering the Mansfield Road, had really large gardens, often with several tall forest trees of various kinds. Two playing fields added to the green spaciousness of the district. Most of the roads had trees planted at regular intervals along each side (lime, chestnut, plane, etc) which, although pruned every three years to mere stumps, were additional feeding and nesting areas.

The most successful species was of course the house sparrow, which was abundant. The starling too, whether probing the lawns and grassy recreational areas or feeding on the scraps put out by householders, was found to be at home and very common, almost every road holding two or three breeding pairs. Their numbers appeared to be limited only by the number of breeding places available.

Because of its retiring nature, the dunnock was not easy to assess, but as each pair seemed able to exist in a territory of three or four gardens in extent, the density must have been considerable, and this was considered to be the third most numerous species in Woodthorpe. The next most successful bird was the blackbird, which had adapted itself to the habitat as efficiently as in both woodland and farmland. Study walks were made for the purpose of locating singing males in territory, and a figure of at least 133 pairs for the 380 acres was obtained.

A careful count of the blue tit was not made and assessment was based mainly on sight records of food-collecting pairs and upon nest reports from people in the district. This method gave a total of 20–30 pairs. Perhaps less adaptable than the blackbird, the song thrush was far less numerous and it was discovered that each pair held a much larger territory. The ratio seemed to be 10 pairs of blackbirds for every one of song thrush, and the assessment for the song thrush population was 14–20 pairs.

The woodpigeon was another difficult species to count because of nest failure but, from the flight displays of the males, it was obvious that pairs were scattered throughout the area. The estimate of 10 pairs could be on the low side in some years.

One of the surprises of the study was the discovery that the greenfinch was evenly spread over the housing areas and was not confined to the open places. The butterfly song and flight display was a feature of walks in the neighbourhood, and the kerbside trees, when pruned, were used as nesting places, with the lush, dense growth giving protection. Up to 12 pairs were located.

In areas of large gardens, especially adjacent to the disused railways, the wren was successful. Away from such areas this species was much thinner on the ground. Assessment was difficult in spite of its loud song and a satisfactory total was not obtainable, but at least 10 pairs were considered as regular. The next most numerous species was the great tit, some 8–9 pairs, although it must be emphasised that most were dependent upon the parks and other wild corners. Actual garden nests were few. During the breeding season most of the robins too deserted the private gardens for safer nesting places in the wilder corners, and the population was considered to be only about 10 pairs.

The swift returned to Woodthorpe regularly around 2 May, and a small colony was using the older houses of the Grange Road area. Later, some spread into the newer houses and numbers were probably controlled by the availability of nest sites. There were no breeding birds in houses where newness or design prevented entry into the roof. The total population was, on average, about 6 pairs.

The positions of the two parks, the two playing fields, and the houses with huge lawns and tall trees were sufficiently widespread to enable the mistle thrush to be evenly distributed and 6 pairs were regular breeders.

Another surprise of this suburban study was the number of goldfinches, at least 6 pairs, which appeared during each spring to settle down to breed. The counting of nests in the autumn when the leaves had fallen helped to confirm breeding. This finch was not disturbed by either people or traffic, and the nests were not confined to quiet, open areas.

The years of the study were a time when the chaffinch population in Nottinghamshire was decreasing and the total of 4–5 pairs probably represents a minimum, as the areas with plenty of trees could have carried more breeding birds.

At the start of the study in 1958, the magpie was represented by one pair which bred in the open, thorny parts to the east, but by 1967 numbers had increased to 3 pairs and this species became bolder and regular around the private gardens, much to the discomfiture of the blackbirds and song thrushes.

The house martin suffered many vicissitudes, due to nest destruction or loss from tidy-minded house-owners and from home-hunting house sparrows. Numbers from year to year were variable, 2–6 pairs. The other hirundines were not well represented at all, though perhaps because of some convenient shed on the allotments to the east (now built over) one pair of swallows was regular to 1967, and the adults ranged over the houses and gardens as far as the Thackeray's Lane–Arno Vale–Breckhill Road roundabout. The sand martin was irregular, with one pair using the sandstone cliff of the disused Daybrook–Gedling railway line at times. This species, incidentally, was regular in small numbers in the Sherwood and Basford districts, 2 miles nearer the city centre.

The stockdove had adapted itself to suburban living and was a contender for garden scraps. Two pairs were usually resident in Woodthorpe, and towards the end of the study were joined by the collared dove. This newcomer to Britain was also at 2 pairs, but was likely to increase.

In the parks and sometimes in the garden areas resembling open woodland the spotted flycatcher bred, 2–3 pairs usually, although there were good and bad years.

Linnets, usually in search of water, visited the gardens from their breeding areas in the wasteland, such as along the disused railways and in the derelict allotments. The linnet, however, was not classed as a species of the housing areas, and other species of Woodthorpe which bred, or were present because of remnant country habitat or the natural amenities of the parks etc, were:

Carrion crow	1–2 pairs	Tawny owl	1 pair
Jackdaw	1–2 pairs	Coal tit	1 pair
Bullfinch	1–2 pairs	Marsh tit	1 pair
Whitethroat	1–2 pairs	Cuckoo	1 pair
Tree sparrow	1–2 pairs	Moorhen	1 pair
Little owl	1–2 pairs	Partridge	1 pair

The few rooks of Arnold, decreasing in numbers down the study years, came to the open areas to feed. One or two willow warbler pairs were fairly regular at first, but their habitat decreased during the study. The loss of the brickyard fields put paid to the breeding tree pipit and the skylark. Occasionally a mallard from the Arnot Park Pond bred well away from the park and then faced the hopeless task of walking its family back to the pond such as from the top area of Breckhill!

To summarise, the birdlife of Woodthorpe was at least 39 breeding species in 1958–9, a total reduced to 36 with the loss of the rough, thorny pasture and the old allotments, but up to 37 with the arrival of the collared dove. This final total can be split into two sections as explained above; (1) 21 species which bred in all habitats and were garden birds; (2) a further 16 species which used the wilder surrounds.

Successful though some of the species were, the main disadvantages of the built-up area, a shortage of good nest sites, heavy predation from the high density of cats, and a shortage of food in varying degrees according to the species and the conditions, was evident even in Woodthorpe.

The privet hedge is favoured for marking garden boundaries in many areas, and is often used by the dunnock, but is only suitable on occasions for others such as the blackbird. All too often the domestic cat destroys the nest and takes the nestlings. A privet hedge is better than none at all and the recent custom of building housing without garden divisions reduces the number of nest sites considerably. There is no remedy for the big numbers of cats, except the cat-proof nest site and, possibly, the planting of thorny evergreens by all lovers of birds. From the Woodthorpe study it was learned that cats do the most damage at the nest and, if predation here could be reduced, the taking of inexperienced birds and killing during the winter by cats would be part of natural wastage.

Food shortage arose in Woodthorpe from three causes. 1, in the breeding-season drought on the sandstone areas the usual prolific worm supply was almost completely lost. A sure sign of drought was the desertion of playing fields by birds at a time when this grassland should be holding many food-hunting blackbirds, song thrushes, mistle thrushes and starlings. Young birds were found to 'go light', and dead ones examined were emaciated. 2, with the blue tits, and possibly the great tit, marsh tit and chaffinch, difficulties were apparent when cold weather checked the growth of foliage and the consequent caterpillar harvest. Being a limited habitat for such species their success rate is based on narrow margins and in these weather conditions there were nest failures of a reduction in the number of young which fledged. The zealous use of pesticides proved to be a grave hazard too. 3, hard winters are a natural hazard, for the average garden, being neat and tidy, offers little in the way of reserve food. The planting of food-bearing trees and shrubs is one answer, while special and continuous feeding by householders can reduce shortage of food. Fortunately, more people are taking an interest in the various species and are learning to specialise in this matter. In Woodthorpe good survival during the savage 1962–3 winter was almost solely due to sustained feeding by the public.

From the above example of Woodthorpe, which possesses a high grade of natural amenity sufficient to allow birdlife to prosper or maintain itself, it is possible to work down the scale, or move inwards to the city centre, to conditions less advantageous for wildlife, until the areas of Victorian terrace housing, the lowest grade, are reached. This type of housing is due for clearance, but where it remains the breeding community of birds is usually restricted to house sparrow, starling, feral pigeon and swift.

The following, give or take a species or two, serves as an indication of the bird-carrying potentiality of the Nottingham conurbation which, by and large, is pleasantly varied right to the city centre, thanks to previous city councillors, who saw the need for open spaces for citizens as well as birds.

Grade 1, over 40 species: Wollaton Park, University grounds, Colwick Woods, Trentside fields and open land.

Grade 2, 35 to 40 species: Woodthorpe, Hungerhill Gardens/Mapperley Hospital, Redhill (Arnold), Wollaton, Bramcote, Valley Road (Sherwood), East Arnold/Mapperley/Gedling.

Grade 3, 25 to 34 species: North Arnold, Bilborough, Broxtowe, Mapperley, Mapperley Park, Ruddington, Chilwell, Toton, Gedling, Arnold.

Grade 4, 15 to 24 species: Clifton Estate, Beeston, Lenton, West Bridgford, The Park (City), Sherwood, Aspley, Wilford, Carlton, Porchester, Thorneywood, Highbury Vale, Colwick Woods Estate.

Grade 5, 5 to 14 species: Beeston Rylands, Sneinton, City Centre, Carrington, Bulwell, Bestwood Estate, Radford, Netherfield.

Grade 6, under 5 species: The Meadows.

Smaller built-up areas in the county, such as Newark, Mansfield, Retford and Worksop, it is anticipated, would have zones from Grades 1 to 4.

At migration time, and during the winter, many species pass through or visit the built-up areas, from grounded warblers to foraging gulls and berry-searching fieldfares, redwings and, in some years, waxwings. The Nottingham conurbation is so varied with intrusions of open land that a birdwatcher remaining within its confines can obtain a formidable list of species.

It is regrettable that during the post-war years from 1946, building has just occurred haphazardly in the city centre, where tall blocks were pushed up indiscriminately, and also in the outlying areas, where the policy seemed to be to drench the acres with housing. In thinking of green corners, bushes, trees and the general ecology of a more natural built-up area, planners and builders would be providing a more satisfying place for both people and the birds so many of them love. The Meadows, bottom of the above list and due to be rebuilt, would blossom as a green haven linked to the Trent Embankment.

MIGRATION

The birdwatcher of Nottinghamshire quickly realises that the county is fortunately placed for seeing something of the great bird movements which take place at certain times of year. Lying east of the Pennines and being part of the lowlands immediately south-west of the southern tip of Scandinavia, Nottinghamshire is only just west of the main bird routes between north-west Europe and Africa via Iberia. A little deflection under certain weather conditions brings many migrant birds to the valleys and woods of Nottinghamshire, enabling the local birdwatcher to see species which, in the ordinary run of things, would require long special journeys.

A CALENDAR OF LOCAL BIRD MOVEMENTS

The calendar demonstrates that bird movements take place in any month of the year. However, true migration does not begin until March, usually after the 8th which seems to mark the end of severe weather in the East Midlands, and there is migration of some kind right through to November except for a short pause in June. Migration within the county is on a broad front according to the species involved and the weather situation prevailing at the

76

time, although the topographical features do tend to make some parts of Nottinghamshire better than others.

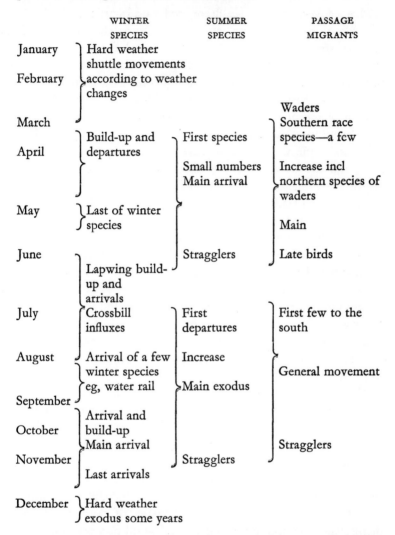

	WINTER SPECIES	SUMMER SPECIES	PASSAGE MIGRANTS
January	Hard weather shuttle movements according to weather changes		
February			
March			Waders Southern race species—a few
April	Build-up and departures	First species	
		Small numbers Main arrival	Increase incl northern species of waders
May	Last of winter species		Main
June	Lapwing build-up and arrivals	Stragglers	Late birds
July	Crossbill influxes	First departures	First few to the south
August	Arrival of a few winter species eg, water rail	Increase	General movement
September		Main exodus	
October	Arrival and build-up Main arrival		Stragglers
November	Last arrivals	Stragglers	
December	Hard weather exodus some years		

In the spring the movements of the Continental species which have wintered in Britain are usually north-east or east. Most English springs have a period of cold, northerly winds which inhibit bird movement and, at such times, our waters, woods, and fields are temporarily thronged with birds such as the lapwing, golden plover, skylark, fieldfare, redwing, starling, chaffinch, brambling, Bewick's swan, etc, waiting for a change of wind. Most of these leave Nottinghamshire at dusk for the North Sea crossing. When the westerly winds prevail these winter visitors just 'melt away', using the following wind as a useful aid for crossing the wastes of the North Sea.

Most of the summer visitors are nocturnal migrants which, in ideal conditions, suddenly appear at their breeding haunts. Unfortunately, the weather of an English spring is rarely ideal for long, and the arrival of the warblers, hirundines, etc, can be a visible phenomenon as they travel overland during the day after having made a landing south of Nottinghamshire. The sight of a wave arrival can be a thrilling experience, when hedgerows, woods, willow holts and waters suddenly swarm with migrants from Africa. These daytime overland movements are usually to the north and north-east, when the Trent Valley is well used, as are the valleys of the Erewash, Leen, Dover Beck and Greet. Against cold northerly winds the valleys offer food and shelter for the insectivorous species. Sometimes spring arrival from the east is noticeable: almost certainly the birds are correcting an earlier drift too far to the east, possibly under the influence of strong westerly winds.

While our own summer species are busy with their first nests, there takes place the passage of the birds which belong to latitudes much further north. Late April and May is the time for these species to travel the flight route. Should an anti-cyclone be stationed over Scandinavia or Germany, they are subjected to easterly winds all the way from Spain, and often with this weather situation England can be under grey skies which, at night, interfere with navigation. Consequently, many of these birds find themselves over southern England and good numbers appear in Nottinghamshire as they correct their flight and head for southern Norway or Sweden.

On such occasions the terns arrive, especially black tern,

common tern and Arctic tern and although they are recorded over most of the county there is a marked concentration along the Trent Valley, where the river seems to offer some comfort or assurance. Such Scandinavian and northern species as the osprey, marsh harrier, sanderling, turnstone, black-tailed godwit, bar-tailed godwit, whimbrel, pied flycatcher and redstart form part of this great movement.

June is very much an early summer month and yet, during the second half, about the time of the haymaking, the first migrant waders head south to pass through Nottinghamshire, where some will dawdle at any wet place which offers food and rest. The species which begin this early departure are usually the common sandpiper, the green sandpiper and the curlew. Snipe and ruff are often close upon their heels.

The NE–SW flight route (page 76) is used by the waders, but also many of them will travel down the east coast of Britain visiting the main wader haunts, and Nottinghamshire is in the path of this often leisurely drift to the SSW. Wetland habitat is now scarce in our county and, because of this lack of tourist catering, the wader numbers are small; but up to 1960 the extensive old-style Nottingham Sewage Farm was a wonderful artificial marsh. The species and numbers of waders visiting this area were recorded as carefully and extensively as possible, with the result that we have a good idea of the migration times of the various waders.

All August and early September is the peak time for the southward migration of the summer and northern species when, as our own countryside, especially the woodland, quietly empties, the arrival of northern birds temporarily replenishes the local supply. Once again the weather situations play an important role. Should the Atlantic depressions hold sway, as they move north-east between Iceland and Scotland, then there is dull watching because the great flow of birds from Scandinavia misses England, probably to travel down the Belgium and Dutch coasts. The classic situation for easterly drift is the positioning of an anticyclone over Scandinavia or northern Europe. Calm conditions and clear skies promote migration movement, and large numbers set off southward on their great nocturnal journey. South of the anti-cyclone, easterly winds will prevail which, if combined with a frontal system associated with low pressure, will create low cloud, rain haze and even thundery outbreaks. The birds, especially the small passerines, lose their sense of direction and the result is a spectacular fall of tired migrants on the east coast. Nottinghamshire receives a share of these, usually willow warblers, chiffchaffs, redstarts, spotted flycatchers and wheatears, plus the rarities such as the red-breasted flycatchers of 1947 and 1950, the barred warbler of 1968 and, more regularly, pied flycatchers and wrynecks. There is an increase in the waders too, when there is a touch of east in the wind, with appearances of such European species as the little stint, Temminck's stint, wood sandpiper, spotted redshank and curlew sandpiper. Tired individuals are to be found in our river valleys, around the fringes of gravel pits and, such is the scarcity of food-providing mud, even at cattle ponds. (Some of these, such as the curlew sandpiper, have been deflected from a migration route much further to the east than the one mentioned on page 76.)

This movement slackens during September, and the large-scale arrival is that of the great numbers of winter visitors from Europe. These can reach Nottinghamshire from the north-east, east or south-east according to the particular crossing of the North Sea. However, records show that most come from the north-east, from Scandinavia, and this is especially noticeable with the routes taken by fieldfare and redwing. Good numbers of starlings and, at times, chaffinches and skylarks seem to make a coastal arrival in the area of the Wash and north Norfolk, perhaps from the South Baltic zone, and later these birds are seen on a westerly course over south Nottinghamshire.

Finally, usually in November or early December, hard weather in north Europe causes the last species to cross the North Sea and brings in the herds of Bewick's swan, a sky spectacular known to Nottinghamshire only since 1954 or thereabouts. The skeins of white-fronted geese often come with them, but whereas many of the swans will rest on our washland pastures, most of the geese pass over. Also at this time there is an increase of goldeneye and goosander which are thought to be of Scandinavian origin.

So far, only the movements of the regular species to Britain and NW Europe have been discussed. Mention must be made of other visitors which come to Nottinghamshire but, in these cases, evidence of their presence is much less strong and the causal weather feature is not always known. There are, for instance, links with the north-western migrants of Iceland and Greenland, and perhaps the strongest evidence that birds of this region pass through Nottinghamshire comes from the regular spring movements of large 'northern' wheaters which occur after the British wheaters have passed through. Undoubtedly some, or most, of these belong to the Greenland race.

The waders of the north-west and the north-east are impossible to differentiate, and yet the black-tailed godwit, whimbrel and redshank present when westerly winds prevail could be birds from Iceland or Greenland instead of from northern Europe. The rare arrival of a grey phalarope is, of course, a much more reliable piece of evidence, and its appearance is usually connected with strong Atlantic gales.

A glance through the systematic list will show that such Mediterranean species as the hoopoe, bee-eater and little egret reach the county, their presence being generally attributed to their having overshot their normal range, or to northward movement by birds of the year.

Finally, there is the arrival of sea birds from time to time, gannets, little auks, petrels and Manx shearwaters, etc, usually the victims of fierce winds circling a deep depression in the Atlantic. Weakened by hunger from day after day of storm and swept on to a lee shore, these vagrants travel helplessly with the wind. Upsetting winds and harsh conditions on the North Sea too can bring in sea birds at times. The Atlantic storms, especially old yet still vigorous hurricanes, are also responsible for the arrival of American species in Britain, of which Nottinghamshire has had a small share.

Below is a summary showing the main findings from ringing recoveries of birds connected with Nottinghamshire and, again, it is emphasised that it is a summary. Obviously, all the recoveries cannot be printed here, and it is not necessary with many, because the findings have been duplicated, triplicated and even repeated a number of times.

MIGRATION ROUTES AND DESTINATIONS

One has only to stand still for five minutes anywhere and watch the sky to discover that at least one bird is going somewhere: not merely from one garden to the next, or from one street to the next, but a definite journey. In or out of the migration seasons, summer or winter, there is always a bird intent on going somewhere. Ringing has helped to elucidate some of these movements and they have been itemised as follows:

1. North (in the spring) and south (in autumn) migration movements of the summer visitors within Britain
2. Foreign recoveries of summer visitors
3. Movements of winter visitors of the north and east
4. Passage migration
5. Hard-weather exodus
6. Exchange of breeding area by summer species
7. Reverse migration
8. Exchange of wintering area
9. Resident species—southward shift
10. Resident species—random dispersal
11. Resident species—movement abroad

1. *North and South Movements of Summer Visitors within Britain (Nottinghamshire Connections)*

The compass directions shown by local ringing reveal routes to and from the south-west, through south to due east. This is not surprising in view of the displacements known to take place under certain adverse weather conditions. However, it is obvious from these routes that flight lines to the south and south-east, through Bedfordshire, Huntingdonshire and other places linked with ringing stations such as the Rye Meads SF, Hertfordshire, Chichester and places in Essex and Kent, represent the standard direction. There could be some positional bias from a concentration of ringers in the Greater London area but, nevertheless, the ringing recoveries support what was already known: that the summer visitors to or from Nottinghamshire favour a southern or south-eastern route within England, and those on other routes (linked with the south-west or east) are in a minority.

Species such as swift, sand martin, swallow, sedge warbler, chiffchaff and lesser black-backed gull have been connected with the south or the south-east of England while moving into or out of the country.

Connections with the south-west are few. A Nottinghamshire reed warbler called in at Jersey in September 1959 on its way back to Africa and, two years later, was recaught at Attenborough.

Most sand martins with local connections are linked with southern England, and the individual caught at Cheltenham in May 1962 and controlled at Scrooby in August 1963, must have been a little off course for once.

These recoveries are examples of summer birds using the main routes into and out of Britain. Sometimes there is error in the spring, perhaps under the influence of westerly winds, when birds travel too far to the east and, in correcting their position, carry out westerly movement. An example of this type of corrected flight comes out of the story of the 20 sand martins which went aboard a fishing vessel near the Dogger Bank in the North Sea on the evening of 2 May 1968. One of the martins died in the night, and its ring showed that it had been ringed as a juvenile at Attenborough on 28 August 1967. Because of lack of information, one must assume that these birds were destined for England and, having failed to enter in the safer south-east, were in trouble over the sea in cloudy, wet, windy weather. A whitethroat, ringed at Attenborough on 7 May, was proved to be on a westerly course when it was killed by a car near Wrexham only a short time afterwards.

2. *Foreign Recoveries of Summer Visitors*

So far only the inland routes suggested by ringing recoveries have been analysed. Recoveries beyond our shores, when mapped, mark the migration route to winter quarters. Obviously the first stage south is France, revealed by an Attenborough swallow at Fort Mahon in the north-east, by a Warsop willow warbler which died at Gatteville, Manche, and by sand martins: one ringed at La Chapelle sur Erdre, Loire Atlantique on its journey south in September 1967 came to Attenborough the following June, while another, a Girton bird, was connected with Bressuire in Deux Sevres.

Recoveries in the Iberian Peninsula confirm the route and there are Spanish ringing results of a Bunny willow warbler with Monteforte de Lemos, Lugo, and of a sand martin of Carlton in Lindrick with Alicante. The reed warblers of the Trent Valley give two

links with Portugal, at Portimao and Lisbon, and then go one
better by linking our county with Morocco, a stage further in the
migration south. An Attenborough sand martin died at Outat el
Hadj, Taza, Morocco in May 1971 while returning north.

From North Africa there is a gap until winter quarters are
shown by recoveries of a 1967 swift, an adult ringed at Attenborough, which was found in East Malawi in December 1969,
and by a number of swallows. Nottinghamshire swallows have
been proved to winter at Johannesburg and Kransberg in the
Transvaal, and further south at two places in the Cape Province.

Some species take a more south-easterly route, avoiding Spain;
a Rufford lesser whitethroat was recovered in Italy.

3. *Movements of Winter Visitors of the North and East*
There is no mystery as to the place of origin of the winter species
whose flight lines in the autumn, if traced back on a map, go to
Scandinavia and the Baltic States. However, ringing recoveries
are more precise. The Continental starling, so evident in the late
autumn and winter, is a useful indicator species for this group of
birds. Easily caught, the starling has provided many recoveries,
and Nottinghamshire is linked with Norway, Sweden, Finland,
Denmark, Belgium, Holland, Germany and, seemingly, strongly
with the USSR (including Estonia), with recoveries at Vitebsk,
Smorgan, Rezhev and Rybatschi. Other good indicators are the
blackbird (Norway, Sweden, Holland, Denmark and Germany)
and the chaffinch (Sweden, Belgium and Germany).

Some of these are birds caught on passage emphasising the
importance of the North European Plain as a major migration
route. Birds of passage from Europe are typified by the siskin
which was ringed at Vannes in France in October 1961 and was
found in Sutton-in-Ashfield a month later, and by the teal, caught
and ringed in Senderbo, Denmark, during November 1967 which
was shot at Clifton two years later. Some bramblings caught in
Nottinghamshire have been linked with central Europe.

Ringing has confirmed what was known, but not proved
locally. Every autumn there is an appearance of water rails in the

wet, marshy places throughout Nottinghamshire, and during the years of the TVBW these were classed as winter visitors from Europe, a fact which was definitely established when a water rail caught and ringed at Clifton in January 1968 was recovered later in the year in Germany.

Similarly, there are the sightings of great spotted woodpeckers in unusual places during the autumn. Usually it is impossible to differentiate them from our own British stock, either because of poor visibility or just lack of opportunity, and such birds are recorded as suspected Continentals. On 15 September 1968 a Continental great spotted woodpecker, a juvenile, appeared at Spurn Point where it was duly caught and ringed at the observatory. Three months later it was found at East Markham and the presence of visiting woodpeckers was proved.

Equally satisfying were the bittern from Poland, the black-headed gull from Sweden, and the common gull from Waika Isle, Russia. Others brought an element of surprise, such as the long-eared owl, born in Holland, which came to Gotham, and the lesser black-backed gull ringed in May in Germany. In the reverse direction, how can it be explained that a juvenile lapwing of the Nottingham Sewage Farm went to Kunya, Pskov, Russia, unless it joined up with Soviet birds wintering in the Trent Valley.

Some recoveries explain little beyond that a bird moved from A to B, and the significance of the change of surroundings requires conjecture. A redpoll ringed in Sherwood Forest during the early spring was later caught in Norfolk: was it on the way back to Europe? To support this theory, another Sherwood Forest redpoll was controlled at Verdenne, Belgium. Some greenfinch recoveries have a similar story, but with a north-east movement. On two occasions greenfinches ringed in Nottinghamshire from wintering flocks have been recovered in March near the coast, at Cleethorpes and Old Goole respectively. Were they heading for Norway or Sweden? Of the wildfowl, mallard and teal caught during the autumn or winter in Norfolk, Essex and Kent one year have turned up in our county another year, as if they were Continental visitors.

An exceptional piece of information came to us when a wintering male blackbird, ringed in Wollaton Park during February 1968, was recaught in Iceland in March 1970. At present it stands alone as evidence of a link with the north-west.

4. *Passage Migrants*

Species which breed well to the north of Britain, and winter well to the south, especially the waders, figure prominently in the annual records, but they have not been well worked by the ringers, partly because of the difficulty in catching them and mainly because Nottinghamshire stopping places are now too scattered and attract too few birds at any one time. The dunlin which rested on the Nottingham Sewage Farm in August 1958 only to be shot at Normcotier, Vendee, France, and the one ringed at Ottenby, Oland, Sweden in August 1961 and controlled at Attenborough three months later, typify these migrants. The ruff ringed on the Nottingham Sewage Farm on 1 September 1962 is not quite so straightforward, as it was shot at Cologna, Verona, Italy, in March 1965 and probably met its end while on the northward journey from Africa.

5. *Hard-Weather Fugitives*

When severe weather comes to Nottinghamshire there is considerable movement by species which rely on soft or snow-free ground. Two snipe, which had been happy on the Nottingham Sewage Farm where they were ringed on 16 December 1961, fled south for safety only to be shot a few days later, one in North France and one in the Pyrenees. Another, shot near Corunna, Spain, in January 1965, probably moved south to avoid severe conditions, although it was ringed in November three years before.

An Attenborough starling of December 1959 which turned up at Hyde, Cheshire, in March 1960, a Goverton blackbird of September 1961 which went to Bodmin, Cornwall, and the 1960 juvenile lapwing of Clumber Park which was recovered on 2 January 1962 at Finisterre, North Spain, were probably refugees from a frozen eastern England.

6. *Exchange of Breeding Area by Summer Species*
This type of movement can only be detected by ringing and is safely confirmed when young are ringed in the nest. One such young swallow, ringed at Nuthall on 23 July 1960, was caught and released at Barnsley on 15 August 1962, well to the north of its birthplace. A young Lambley swallow was caught while breeding at Larne, Northern Ireland, in the following year.

Sand martins have been proved to change their breeding area from one year to the next, and also some have moved from one colony to another colony during the breeding season. Such birds must be non-breeders, unmated or failed breeders. Possibly a straightforward example of breeding-area exchange is presented by the juvenile sand martin ringed at Edwinstowe in July 1969 and controlled at Fairburn, Yorkshire, the following May.

7. *Birds on Reverse Migration*
This interesting phenomenon of migrant birds moving in an aberrant fashion, that is going the opposite way from their normal migrational direction, is well known, and ringing has proved that it occurs among many, or most, species. A classical example of this with local connections was a juvenile garden warbler which was ringed at Benacre, Suffolk, on 30 August 1965; presumably the ringer assumed that it was moving south. The bird, however, came to Cropwell Bishop where it was killed by a car on 13 September 1965. Similarly, a nestling swallow ringed in June 1970 at Mansfield Woodhouse moved north and was controlled at Brough, Yorks, during the following September.

There are no local ringing examples of a much rarer occurrence, of summer species returning to their breeding areas only to meet wintry weather and being forced to retreat south again.

8. *Birds Exchanging Wintering Area*
The large number of winter species which flood into Britain every autumn do not go to the same area of the country every year. This change of wintering area may be due to mere chance or can be due to the weather prevailing at the time of the migration.

Local changes which come into this category are portrayed by the starling of Goverton, Bleasby, in 1959 which was recovered in Leicester in early April 1960, and by the Mexborough starling of winter 1967 which was at Clipstone in 1970. A Clumber greenfinch could fit into this group too. It was caught from a flock in March 1969 and, the following winter, was controlled at Skelton, Yorks. A chaffinch at Leigh, Lancs, in March 1968 was controlled at Attenborough in February 1969. A jack snipe of October 1969 at Holbeck was shot in County Down, Ireland, in January 1972.

A variation of this change in wintering area occurs when a European species winters in Britain one year and in south Europe in another. Redwings and fieldfares will do this and two Nottinghamshire ringed blackbirds seem to fit this pattern. One, caught in Clumber Park on 9 March 1964 at the end of winter, was recovered at Branzi, north Italy, in the following autumn, and a Costock adult blackbird, ringed in January 1959 was recovered in north Britanny, France, during February 1962. It is possible, however, that this bird had been in Britain and went to France because of the severe weather. Interpretation, as well as winter migration, has its hazards!

9. *Resident Species—Southward Shift*
So far, only birds which spend a part of the year with us have been considered, and now it is the turn of the resident species, those which belong to Britain and are only partially migratory. Some species move to a position south of their breeding area, in others some birds, but not all, disperse from the area of their birth, yet other species leave the country and can be classed as summer visitors; and, of course, there are those which do not move very much.

A kestrel ringed at Langholm, Dumfries on 20 June 1968 came to grief at Oxton during its second southward movement in 1969, while a locally born kestrel of South Notts died near Colchester in February 1970. Some of the redpolls, in large numbers at the end of winter in Sherwood Forest, have been proved by ringing to belong to Northumberland and south Scotland.

10. *Resident Species—Random Dispersal*

Under this heading comes the normal spreading-out of young birds, such as the two young barn owls ringed in a nest near Retford which were killed by cars at Ranby and Pinxton respectively. A little owl had a brief life commencing at Retford in June 1963 and ending on a gamekeeper's gibbet (in spite of protection by law) near Worksop in April 1964.

Mute swan recoveries show a fairly neat dispersal within the counties of Staffordshire, Derbyshire, Nottinghamshire, Lincolnshire and Yorkshire. The River Trent, plus possibly the Idle and the Witham, seem to form the highways along which the swans move. North Nottinghamshire has been linked by ringing mainly with Yorkshire and Lincolnshire, while the Trent Valley of the Nottingham area has main connections with the mute swans of Burton-on-Trent, and with Whittington and Blithfield, Staffordshire.

There have been numerous local recoveries such as two moorhens, one of which travelled from the Nottingham Sewage Farm to Long Eaton, and the other from Retford to Saxilby. Of the great tits there was one which came from near Lincoln to Woodborough and one which exchanged Dale Abbey, Derbyshire for Radcliffe-on-Trent. Other examples chosen at random are:

	From	*To*
Heron	Galley, Staffs	Newark
Kingfisher	Minworth, Warwick	Beeston
Long-tailed tit	Armthorpe, Yorks	Retford
Long-tailed tit	Ailsworth, Northants	Arnold
Mistle thrush	East Leake	Glenfield, Leics
Pied wagtail	Glossop, Derbys	Attenborough
Dunnock	Attenborough	Rushden, Northants
Reed bunting	Trent Valley	Very local movement, except one which went to Lancashire from Attenborough and two to Devon
House sparrow	Gibraltar Point, Skegness	North Wheatley
House sparrow	Ruddington	Burton-on-Trent

The local Canada geese have been ringed during their moulting period for several seasons, local ringers combining under the leadership of John McMeeking to obtain the maximum results. Local movements were revealed by the discovery of a Kedleston Hall, Derbyshire, bird and by birds from Wakefield, Yorks. The greatest surprise was that some were connected with the strange moult migration to Beauly Firth, Scotland, a recently discovered phenomenon amongst Canada geese, which until now were considered to be sedentary.

The black-headed gulls born in Nottinghamshire make a useful go-between from the resident species which move within Britain to those which go beyond our shores, because these have done both. About 50 ringing recoveries of Nottinghamshire birds were scrutinised (Flegg and Cox, 1972) and revealed that there was a random dispersal from breeding areas. However, most of the first-year birds moved westerly (NW, W, SW), whereas the adult birds were almost equally connected with NW, W, S, and E. Many, especially adults and older birds, do not move far from their breeding areas. Recoveries in Britain have been widespread:

North: Glasgow, Preston, Barrow in Furness, Southport, Carlisle, Wakefield, Doncaster.

West and Central: Bridgnorth, Rhyl, Holbeach, Sleaford, Droitwich, Martlesham (Suffolk), Boston, Ashton under Lyne, Kirkby on Bain and in Ireland.

South and South-west: Dawlish, Newton Abbot, Bognor Regis, Newbury, Burnham on Sea.

A Heptonstall, Yorks, bird came to Nottinghamshire.

Beyond our shores, local black-headed gulls went to Minho, Portugal, and amazingly one reached Port Etienne in Mauritania, Africa.

11. *Resident Species—Moving Abroad*

A juvenile song thrush ringed 7 August 1958 at Watnall was killed at Gironde in France on 3 March 1960. Another song thrush, a nestling of Goverton, Bleasby, of July 1958, was recovered at Aveiro, Portugal, on 7 February 1960. The lifespan and demise of these two birds is very similar, and they may have moved south because of hard weather, although the winter to February and March 1960 was not severe.

Our linnets show a definite tendency to move out and, possibly, our goldfinches also. Ringing has shown clearly that many of our linnets migrate to France and to the Mediterranean area, through recoveries from Biarritz and Landes, France, from Cagliari, Sardinia, and from Spain.

There are other recoveries which defy a precise interpretation, such as that of the tree sparrow which came to Collingham from Liège in Belgium. It was four years of age and present in the breeding season, so it may have been a Nottinghamshire bird which went south for some reason, or it could have been a Belgian bird which dispersed north into England via the Straits of Dover to become a settled immigrant. Birds are individuals, and it is quite possible that some move by whim; hence that commonplace sight of a bird going somewhere beyond the horizon!

Systematic List of
THE BIRDS OF
NOTTINGHAMSHIRE
1825–1973

(With summary of status to 1970, unless otherwise indicated)

Assessment of the 19th-century and early 20th-century records for this list was made easier in that so many of the unusual species which came to Nottinghamshire were shot. However, some did not fall into this definite category and, consequently, judgement has been made on modern lines as with sight records and not with corpses.

On status, the same method of presentation has been used as in the *Provisional Check-list of the Birds of Nottinghamshire for the Period 1911–1960*, but the reader must bear in mind the reference to numbers and distribution as amplified in the preceding chapters.

The definitions on status are:

NUMBERS

Breeding Species (resident or summer visitor)

Abundant: numbers too big to be easily recorded. Every outing in suitable habitats reveals frequent flocks of hundreds or thousands or single birds and/or groups constantly in sight.

Common: almost all outings in suitable habitats reveal frequent flocks usually under 100, *or* single birds/groups seen at frequent intervals.

Fairly common: most outings in suitable habitats reveal one or more flocks usually under 50, *or* one or more single birds/groups.

Uncommon: outings in suitable habitats rarely reveal more than one single bird or group.

Scarce: numbers so small that only prolonged search normally reveals presence even in suitable habitats. Probably fewer than 20 pairs in county.

Rare: probably fewer than 5 pairs in the county.

All species listed as breeding are known or believed to do so every year unless shown as:

Most years: breeds 7–9 years in 10
Irregular: breeds 4–6 years in 10
Occasional: breeds 1–3 years in 10
Exceptional breeding records are listed individually.

Non-Breeding Species (*winter visitor, passage migrant or vagrant*)
    Abundant, common, fairly common as defined for breeding species.
    Uncommon: total observed in each year under 100.
    Scarce: total observed under 20 each year.
    Rare: total observed under 5 each year.
    All species listed are known or believed to occur every year unless shown as:

Most years: occurs 7–9 years in 10
Irregular: occurs 4–6 years in 10
Occasional: occurs 1–3 years in 10

    The total number of occurrences is shown, where it is up to 12 for the period under review.

DISTRIBUTION

Numbers described can be found in suitable habitats throughout the county unless specific areas are quoted or noted as:
    Thinly distributed: numbers not adequate to fill all suitable areas in each year, or
    Local: population regularly concentrated in certain parts of the county while similar habitat elsewhere is not occupied.

DATES OF THE REGULAR SUMMER AND WINTER VISITORS

These are given except where the birds are present throughout the year, as follows:
  Summer visitors: spring to autumn
  Winter visitors: autumn to spring

DENSITIES

(*Optimum for the most suitable habitat and at a time of full populations*)

These have been attempted for the bird communities of farmland and woodland, and for some of the species of the urban/suburban habitats. Basic knowledge now built up is sufficient to present some of the chief species by density, or rather by a standard using a comparative density. It must be pointed out that in reality there is no fixed density: the cycles of good and bad conditions must make the bird populations differ from year to year. Severe winters can drastically reduce the resident species, which then recover over a number of years, while the summer visitors can be affected by a disastrous migration causing a decrease above that of ordinary wastage.

The varying conditions on farmland and in woodland mentioned in the chapters on habitat, and the changes in land usage, also affect population.

Because it is thought to be easier to adjust downwards according to the quality of the habitat, optimum densities have been quoted for the most suitable living area at a time of full populations. It is hoped that these density ratings will inspire Nottinghamshire ornithologists to concentrate on this aspect in the future, with the ultimate aim of producing maps for each species.

This list follows the Wetmore Order, 1952, and is in accord with the annual bird reports of the Trent Valley Bird Watchers. Nomenclature is as shown in the BOU *The Status of Birds in Britain and Ireland*, 1971.

Black-throated diver   Gavia arctica (Linnaeus)
Rare passage migrant and winter visitor.

12 records (4, Whitaker, but only 1 date, 1848; 8, TVBW—1947, 1954, 1956, 1960, 1961, 1963, 1970 and 1973). Of these records, 10 have been on or very near the River Trent and the remaining 2 were in the Dukeries. Inclusive dates: 4 Nov–25 April.

Great northern diver   Gavia immer (Brünnich)
Rare winter visitor.

6 records (2, Whitaker, but only 1 date, 1853; 4, TVBW—

1946, 1947, 1959 and 1970). 5 of these were in the Trent Valley and the sixth on the Welbeck Great Lake. 6 Dec–13 Feb.

Red-throated diver *Gavia stellata (Pontoppidan)*
Rare passage migrant and winter visitor.

16 records (6, Whitaker; 10, TVBW. Average is 1 every 2–3 years since 1947).

Of the 24 definitely identified, 16 were in the Trent Valley, 3 visited the Mansfield (King's Mill) Reservoir, and the rest were on or near the Dukeries waters. 1 Nov–12 June.

Great crested grebe *Podiceps cristatus (Linnaeus)*
Fairly common summer visitor. Usually rare winter visitor.

Sterland only knew of one record of a pair for his area up to 1869. Whitaker reported this species as very uncommon until afforded the protection of the Bird Act and then, from the years just before 1890, he showed how the waters of Nottinghamshire became a stronghold for breeding. A further big increase in numbers followed the development of the Trent Valley gravel pits.

Census Results
1949 110–120 adults present on 23 out of 26 waters visited. A large proportion of these did not breed.

1955 29–32 breeding pairs were part of 101–110 'census' adults recorded on 30 waters visited.

1965 233–236 adults present on 27–28 waters out of 185 waters/ areas visited.

At the turn of the year 0–3 birds is the normal total, increased by a few more arrivals from the coast if the weather is mild during January, and to 1970 up to 18 birds have been recorded. According to the weather prevailing there is further arrival in February which, by the middle Sunday of the month (wildfowl-counts day when most waters are visited) can range from 8% to 38% of the total breeding stock. March sees a rapid build-up of numbers. After the breeding season some have left Nottinghamshire by mid-September and the exodus continues steadily into November.

Red-necked grebe   Podiceps griseigena (Boddaert)
Rare winter visitor mainly, but 2 June records.

22 or so records (6–7 Whitaker; 1 pre-TVBW; 16, TVBW). Except for one bird at the Lound gravel pit all have been in the Trent Valley.

Extremes of the inclusive dates for usual reports are 22 September–12 April, normally condensed to January–March. The exceptional June dates were in 1850 and 1968.

Slavonian grebe   Podiceps auritus (Linnaeus)
Rare winter visitor and occasional passage migrant.

Around 26 records of which 20 were TVBW.

16 of the above were seen in the Trent Valley.

Inclusive dates 19 November–12 April, but 1 summer record (Whitaker).

Black-necked grebe   Podiceps nigricollis Brehm
Rare winter visitor and passage migrant.

46 records (2 only, Whitaker; 44, TVBW). Whitaker found it the rarer of the two black and white grebes, which is opposite to TVBW findings. The Trent Valley was visited by 35 of the above birds and the rest were for the Mansfield and Dukeries areas.

Appearances fall into two distinct phases: 1, summer arrivals, usually immature birds, appear between July and September, and 2, winter visitors are observed from about November to March and are associated with disturbed or hard weather. 4 July–4 April.

> *Slavonian/Black-necked grebes*   Indefinite records concerning one or other of the above species have occurred fairly frequently, making the above totals minimal.

Little grebe   Tachybaptus ruficollis (Pallas)
Fairly common resident.

No organised counts have ever been carried out in Nottinghamshire for this species. The TVBW records have note of 32 regularly used breeding sites which carry about 49 pairs and this excludes lost waters (Wilford Marsh, Dunkirk Marsh, Gedling

Colliery Flash and Salterford Dam) which held up to 26 pairs.
Taking into account some 26 other suitable waters, the county's
population could be around 80 pairs. One fact is certain: there
must have been over 100 pairs at breeding stations in 1954–6.

Leach's petrel Oceanodroma leucorrhoa (Vieillot)
Storm-driven.
    Single birds 1840, 1878, 1888, 1900, 1906, 1910 and 6 birds in
1952. September, October, November and December are the
months named.

Storm petrel Hydrobates pelagicus (Linnaeus)
Storm-driven.
    12 records (7, Whitaker; 2, Wollaton Hall Museum; 2, TVBW)
1843, 1845, 1861, 1870, 1872, 1876, 2 between 1888–99, 1909,
1945, 1957, 1973. May, October, November and December are
the only months mentioned.

Manx shearwater Puffinus puffinus (Brünnich)
Rare vagrant.
    7 records (3, Whitaker; 1, Wollaton Hall Museum; 3, TVBW)
1888, 1891, 1899, 1924, 1950, 1952, 1967. 1 occurred in June, but
most were during September, the time when the birds of the year
can be swept inland soon after leaving the nest burrow.

Fulmar Fulmarus glacialis (Linnaeus)
Rare vagrant.
    1 in 1971.

Gannet Sula bassana (Linnaeus)
Rare vagrant.
    27 records (12, Whitaker; 15, TVBW). February, July and
August are the only months when this species has not occurred in
Nottinghamshire.

Page 101 (*left*) Wren; (*right*) Robin

Page 102 (above) Reed warbler; *(below)* sedge warbler

Cormorant   Phalacrocorax carbo (Linnaeus)
Scarce vagrant.

Occurs most years and at any time of the year, regular 1954–73. Whitaker listed 4 reports, but numerous TVBW records. Most seen in the Trent Valley. One, 4 April 1972, had the white head and neck of the Continental race.

Shag   Phalacrocorax aristotelis (Linnaeus)
Rare vagrant.

11 reports (1851; c 1867; 1923; 1924; 1925, Whitaker; 1945; 1947; 1954; 1957; 1962; 1972, TVBW). February, April, July, September and November are the months of 6 of the occurrences.

Heron   Ardea cinerea Linnaeus
Fairly common resident.

This species has survived many vicissitudes in the county. Sterland only mentioned the small Thoresby heronry of 4 or 5 nests which the keepers shot up and destroyed in 1856, because the depredations of these 8 or 10 birds were so great!

Whitaker suggested that there were a number of heronries, but only mentioned East Stoke where, under the benign eye of Sir M. Bromley Wilson, some 40 to 50 pairs bred, our largest heronry, as it continued to be for another 43 years. Stanford Hall had a successful heronry too, with 35 nests in 1916 and 17 in 1924. In 1928 a national census of heronies revealed the following nests for Nottinghamshire: Stanford Hall, 30; East Stoke, 28–30; Colwick Woods, 14 (about 12 in 1911); Serlby Park, 7; Clumber Park, 5 (none before 1926); Thoresby, 4 (restarted probably 1870 and 10 by 1907). Total, 88–90.

Apart from normal fluctuations due to hard winters, the numbers of herons seemed reasonably assured until 1950 when the Trent Valley birds came under attack from man. Unhappily East Stoke was first and, although there were 41 nests in 1950, broken eggs and an injured adult bird clearly pointed to some human interference. Only 12 pairs attempted to breed the following spring when they too were molested and the long, successful saga of the East Stoke herons came to an end.

For the next 2 years Colwick Park carried these extra birds from East Stoke increasing to 66 pairs by 1952, but work on the flood-prevention scheme caused interference and some tree felling. The overall population was still around 90 pairs for Nottinghamshire at this time. The Colwick numbers slumped to 13 pairs in 1954, to 5 pairs by 1957, and the heronry ceased to exist in 1959.

In the Trent Valley the herons found sanctuary at Rolleston, where the colony rose from 20+ pairs in 1953 to 43 pairs in the following year and remained at 38–42 pairs until this heronry too was attacked and destroyed to become extinct in 1962, and so, apart from an attempt by a handful of birds near Newark, the Vale of Trent lost its breeding herons. News of 3 pairs at Kingston and 2 pairs at Bunny during the years 1957–62 suggested that there might be a comeback in South Nottinghamshire, but these birds failed to prosper.

While the Trent Valley was losing its herons the Dukeries at first appeared to be making good the loss, with an increase to over 40 nests in 1953 at the Clumber heronry. Then this big estate was vacated by the Army and the owners, the National Trust, began to open it up. Herons and the public are not compatible and the Clumber herony no longer existed in 1957.

Following the extremely severe winter of 1962–3 the numbers of herons in Nottinghamshire were (in pairs): Osberton, 6; Thoresby, 3; Welbeck, 3; Carburton, 3; Serlby, 1. Total, 16.

Because of waterway pollution from town effluent, industrial waste, persistent farming poisons and artificial fertiliser residues, the heron did not show any rapid increase following the 1962–3 winter, reflecting its position at the end of the food chain. However, the rivers and streams are slowly improving, and the phenomenal run of mild winters after 1962–3 reduced winter loss just when it was most needed; in 1970, 46 pairs of herons were breeding in Nottinghamshire, all in Zone 2. All that now seems necessary is a safe site in the Trent Valley to bring back the heron to 80–90 pairs.

The first record of a foreign heron in Nottinghamshire came when an emaciated bird was picked up beside the River Smite near Whatton-in-the-Vale on 21 October 1972. It had been ringed in the nest at Rana, Bildoy, Norway, on 5 April 1972.

Purple heron   Ardea purpurea Linnaeus
Rare vagrant.
   3 reports: 1868, late 19th century, 1972.

Little egret   Egretta garzetta (Linnaeus)
Rare vagrant.
   1, 1970.

Great white egret   Egretta alba (Linnaeus)
Rare vagrant.
   1 shot, before 1838 (Whitaker).

Squacco heron   Ardeola ralloides (Scopoli)
Rare vagrant.
   2 records, 1871 and 1944.

Night heron   Nycticorax nycticorax (Linnaeus)
Rare vagrant.
   2 records, 1820 and 1968.

Little bittern   Ixobrychus minutus (Linnaeus)
Rare vagrant.
   4 records (Whitaker, 1870, 1872, 1908, 1921)

Bittern   Botaurus stellaris (Linnaeus)
Rare winter visitor.
   Occurs most years (11 reports, Whitaker; 28 reports, 1950–73, TVBW).
   This species can appear almost anywhere in the various types of wetland habitat, especially the Continental visitor, which is not addicted to dense reed beds and can tolerate human habitation. One once lived in the ditches and on the grass verge of the Fosse Way until it forgot to look right one day!

An early bird came on 7 August and stayed at Attenborough for a month. Some arrive from September to November, but December is revealed as the main arrival period when, it is proved, Continental birds come to avoid severe European weather. Last dates are usually in March with one, 17 April 1968, exceptionally late.

White stork   Ciconia ciconia (Linnaeus)
Rare vagrant.
   3 reports (Whitaker, 1825, 1829, 1915).

Black stork   Ciconia nigra (Linnaeus)
Rare vagrant.
   1 in 1871.

Spoonbill   Platalea leucorodia Linnaeus
Rare vagrant.
   6 reports, 1831, 1843, 1847, late 19th century, 1924, 1952.

Glossy ibis   Plegadis falcinellus (Linnaeus)
Rare vagrant.
   1 shot 1909.

Mallard   Anas platyrhynchos Linnaeus
Common resident. Winter visitor.
   This duck is ubiquitous and can be found breeding throughout the county wherever there is sufficient suitable habitat to bring up the young, this nursery water may be a slow stream, lake or farmland pond, reservoir or gravel pit. Some pairs nest a considerable distance from water, for example in woodland involving a walk of a quarter of a mile or more for the young. In the TVBW annual report for 1969 the status of the mallard was reviewed and an estimate of 1,000 to 1,300 adults was suggested as the breeding population for Nottinghamshire, bearing in mind the difficulties of assessing this widespread species.
   Following a period of good observation and recording throughout the county during the 1960s, the optimum winter peak population was assessed at 5,000 to 6,000 birds and, as if to sup-

port this, the wildfowl count total for November 1970 was 5,041 birds.

The 1969 review concluded that the mallard was standing up well to the pressures of the times, such as the increase in the use of waters for fishing and boating, water pollution, break-up of large estates where breeding conservation was possible and from more shooting by syndicates and unauthorised gunners.

The time of arrival of the winter visitors depends upon the weather situation on the Continent; the birds move from there when a period of cold, either frosts or snow, makes the wetlands inhospitable. Early autumn arrival is often masked by the big numbers of local birds and the main Nottinghamshire peak is usually late in the year.

Teal   Anas crecca Linnaeus
Scarce in summer. Fairly common winter visitor.

As a breeding species the teal has never been numerous during the years covered by Whitaker and the TVBW. Doubtless it is overlooked to some extent but, even at the best time of the year when the female has her brood, very few are recorded. This species has not taken to the gravel-pit type of habitat for breeding.

The teal is better known as a winter visitor, appearing at first in small numbers during the summer and gradually increasing into the autumn when the main arrival occurs. Favoured areas of shallow water in the past (Nottingham Sewage Farm, Wilford Marsh and the Dunkirk Marsh) were lost, but new wet areas in the Idle Valley helped to compensate. The lower Trent Valley when in a flooded state also holds good numbers. In December 1970 the total wildfowl count gave 2,051 birds, the highest number recorded by the TVBW under optimum conditions. Without the floodwater and relying upon normal lakes, reservoirs and gravel pits etc, the average maximum for very recent times would be approximately 1,000 birds, only a small percentage of these using gravel pits.

Departure is mainly in March, but can be delayed by wintry weather until early April.

Garganey   Anas querquedula Linnaeus
Rare summer visitor.

The breeding requirements of the garganey are similar to those of the teal and, as the county is not well-endowed with shallow water areas, numbers are restricted. However, this summer visitor will use the gravel-pit habitat. It is certainly overlooked but allowing for this numbers are always small. There is evidence of a gradual increase and expansion in England from 1945–8 (J. L. F. Parslow, 1967) and certainly the suitable wetland areas near Nottingham held garganey regularly from 1944 into the 1950s. These wet areas eventually disappeared and so did the garganey. Sterland found a deserted duck's nest near Ollerton in 1855 and from the size of the eggs and their buff colour adjudged them to be garganey; no birds were seen and the record is hardly con-clusive. The first definite breeding was in 1945 in the Trent Valley.

During the last 27 years there was one very early arrival, on 24 February 1952, 11 March arrivals from 9 to 29 March and 11 first dates in April. In 2 years the first birds were seen as late as May, and for 2 years no records were made. Similarly, for the same years, last dates were in August on 9 occasions and in September 14 times, mainly from 3rd to 14th. Latest date was 29 September.

Gadwall   Anas strepera Linnaeus
Rare in summer. Scarce winter visitor.

Breeding was first proved in 1968 in the Dukeries where 1 or 2 pairs are centred, and the first breeding in the Trent Valley was in 1973.

As a winter visitor it has been regular to the Dukeries Lakes and fairly regular elsewhere. Before the presence of birds during the breeding season, say before 1960, records showed arrival from August, and especially from October. March was a favoured time for leaving, with delays into April due to bad weather.

Wigeon   Anas penelope Linnaeus
Fairly common winter visitor. Very occasional summer birds, April–August.

Whitaker recorded breeding at Moorgreen by a slightly wounded female and its drake (late 19th century).

The wintering birds appear in small numbers in the summer, with a gradual increase to the end of the year. This autumn arrival is most variable, depending it is thought on the weather prevailing in Europe. The wigeon's favourite habitat is the marshy meadowland where grassland and open water are available plus, of course, good shallow areas. These conditions prevail at flood-time and it is then that the big numbers appear in the valleys (maximum count, 2,720 birds, mid-February 1972).

Whitaker wrote that goodly numbers frequented the larger Nottinghamshire lakes during the 19th century. The TVBW has never found the Dukeries Lakes favoured by wigeon and only small numbers frequent the other waters known to Whitaker, eg Moorgreen Reservoir, Mansfield Reservoir and the Newstead Abbey lakes. The larger gravel pits have attracted better numbers mainly as rest areas, of which the protected Attenborough Reserve has been most successful. Under dry, mild conditions the wintering population can be small, just a few hundreds.

Departure begins in March and most have gone by early April, exceptionally by mid-April. A few stragglers linger into early May.

American wigeon   Anas americana Gmelin
Rare vagrant.
   1 in 1969.

Pintail   Anas acuta Linnaeus
Uncommon winter visitor.

The thousands which congregate on the Ouse Washlands demonstrate this species' habitat preference, one shared by wigeon and teal. For some reason our floodland, although suitable for the two last-named species, does not attract the pintail in any numbers. Our maximum is 124 during the severe weather of 1947 and only 60 during milder winters. Normally it visits lakes, reservoirs and gravel pits in very small numbers. Whitaker knew it similarly as a 'scarce duck'.

From 1943 to 1970 the summer arrival, from July to August, took place in 9 years while first records were in September for 9 other years. First arrivals were delayed until October on 4 occasions. Sometimes numbers were so small that nothing significant could be ascertained. Departure usually takes place in March with some lingering until May. Summering birds were recorded occasionally.

Shoveler   Anas clypeata (Linnaeus)
Now uncommon summer visitor; formerly fairly common. Uncommon winter visitor.

Whitaker's earliest date for this species was Sterland's report of a male at Thoresby on 24 October 1854. Breeding was recorded from 1874 (Whitaker) and by 1887 10 pairs were present in one valley near Clipstone, and presumably other pairs were scattered around Nottinghamshire.

There is no information on breeding status for the early part of this century but, with the Nottingham Sewage Farm well developed and other areas being suitable in the Trent Valley, it is possible that an increase took place. Certainly they were present on the sewage farm during the 1930s and post-breeding gatherings topped 100 during the next decade, eg 140 on 23 September 1944; 100, July 1945 and 200 by September; 300–400, end of August 1951.

So from possibly the 1930s, certainly the 1940s, to the early 1950s, the Nottingham area (including the sewage farm and various wet places to Attenborough) was a breeding stronghold with 30–40 pairs present every year. The large numbers from 1944 represent the beginning of systematic watching on the sewage farm: quite probably the shoveler was successful there before even the 1930s. Elsewhere in Nottinghamshire the shoveler stock consisted of scattered pairs, probably totalling some 10–12 on average for the period during and just after World War II. With the modernisation of the sewage farm, the draining and industrial-isation at Dunkirk and the draining of the Wilford Marsh, the shoveler correspondingly decreased, until by the late 1950s only a few pairs remained. In the 1970s the situation is back to that of Whitaker's time, with scattered pairs about the county except that the gravel industry does provide a little extra habitat. Generally speaking the breakdown of our small breeding popula-tion would be: Trent Valley, 6 pairs; Idle Valley, 6; Dukeries, 3; elsewhere, 3; total 18 pairs.

Only small numbers winter in Nottinghamshire, usually a maximum of 30–50 birds, but in some years there are less and occasionally more. Excluding September totals previously dis-cussed, which include local birds, December 1956 had the greatest number with 98. Wintering shoveler range widely and are re-corded on most types of waters.

Movements of this species are more clearly understood when it is stressed that two populations are concerned: 1, the breeding population which arrives in March, presumably from some milder locality, and after showing a peak in August or early September departs or disperses; 2, the wintering birds from Europe, their peak arrival being usually in the late autumn, the time varying according to the weather.

Mandarin duck   Aix galericulata (Linnaeus)
Rare vagrant.

In view of this species' feral status in part of Britain, the recent presence of individuals (1963 and 1972) is recorded here, although both were considered to be escaped birds.

Red-crested pochard   Netta rufina (Pallas)
Rare vagrant.

Recorded in 11 years of the 19 from 1955 to 1973.

Truly wild birds appear during the autumn and winter. There are others which are wanderers or escaped birds from collections of wildfowl, and those recorded in 1959, 1961, 1964, 1965, 1966, 1968 and August 1973 were probably in this latter category.

Scaup   Aythya marila (Linnaeus)
Scarce passage migrant and winter visitor.

Whitaker considered this species very rare, and recorded some 12 reports to 1930. TVBW have found it more regular in small numbers, with most appearing during hard weather. Others are often gale-driven wanderers at migration times, winter maximum is c 14.

In recent years there have been reports of sluggish birds associating with the tufted duck and these individuals, lacking true scaup wildness, are thought to be escaped birds from collections or scaup-type hybrids (tufted × pochard, etc).

Scaup have been seen on all types of waters, but the truly wild birds have usually appeared on the Trent or at adjacent gravel pits.

Tufted duck   Aythya fuligula (Linnaeus)
Now fairly common in the breeding season and common in winter.

When Whitaker went to live at Rainworth in 1872 he observed that this species was breeding and published the fact in *The Field*. The news caused quite a stir, although the tufted duck had been breeding regularly since the 1830s in Nottinghamshire, where Whitaker claims it first bred in England. The county population 1872–1900, estimating from Whitaker, must have been fairly considerable, as he noted nearly 20 pairs about Rainworth plus others at Newstead, Rufford, Osberton, Clumber, Park Hall, Papplewick and Annesley. Doubtless the birds benefited from the peace and protection of well-keepered estates.

These established waters have continued to be breeding areas during the 20th century; times have changed, but even Clumber Park, often thronged with thousands of people plus many nosing dogs, still holds several breeding pairs.

In 1953 a family party (a female and 6 youngsters) was seen on the Besthorpe gravel pits, the first proof of breeding in this type of habitat and an extension from the known breeding areas. Since then the tufted duck has exploited the gravel-pit type of water to increase, and perhaps more than double, the Nottinghamshire breeding population. Sometimes they nest semi-colonially; nest-predation from crow, fox and egg-collecting human can be heavy at times. During the late 1960s to 1970 broods have been regularly reported from at least 19 areas, and in 1970 64 broods were counted in 13 of these areas, with the possibility of a minimum of 15 more broods from the other unrecorded waters.

The wintering population has also shown an increase since wildfowl counting began after World War II. Drainage, changes in usage, and increased acreage, etc, have affected the numbers, but the tufted duck has enjoyed a population boom. In 1955–6 the total for 18 Nottinghamshire waters was 200, which can be compared with 1971–2 when 1,578 were on 22 waters.

Because of our own breeding stock it has never been easy to time precisely the arrival and departure of the winter visitors from Europe. Arrival is from September continuing to a peak in December or January. Hard weather causes an exodus of some and, if this happens, a minor peak can occur at winter's end, of birds pausing while on their way back into Europe probably from Ireland. Final departure is in April, but it can be delayed into May.

Pochard   *Aythya ferina (Linnaeus)*

Rare in summer, irregular breeder, although difficult to prove every year. Fairly common winter visitor.

Sterland never mentioned this species for his forest area which included Thoresby Hall, while Whitaker knew it as a regular winter visitor to Nottinghamshire mainly in small parties. During the early days of the TVBW recording it was classed as a winter visitor, until 1945 when young birds were seen on the Mansfield Reservoir. From then till 1954 it was considered as an occasional breeder. However, from 1955 to 1970 the pochard was proved to breed in 12 years out of the 16 when a nest and eggs and 18 broods were recorded. So breeding is now less irregular and, because the small numbers involved makes proof of breeding difficult to obtain, more birds may be overlooked. For some reason the pochard has not exploited the gravel-pit habitat as well as the tufted duck has done, although 66% of the above breeding pairs were at gravel pits and significantly 11 of them were at the well-watched Attenborough Reserve.

The pochard was nearly as numerous as the tufted duck during the early years of the autumn-winter wildfowl counts but gradually, during the late 1960s, its numbers fell behind. It increased more rapidly from 1970 and topped the 1,000 mark in early 1972. As with the tufted duck, it will be interesting to see if the high numbers are maintained following a period with hard winters.

The resident birds tend to confuse the dates of first arrivals in late summer, and the last departures of winter visitors in spring. There is, however, a detectable influx during July–August. Very occasionally there is a sharp increase during September, eg 313 birds in September 1968, but this is exceptional and the general trend is for a steady increase during the early autumn to a peak in late October or early November. Considerable departure comes during March but, if the weather is wintry, the exodus can be delayed until April.

Ferruginous duck *Aythya nyroca* (*Güldenstädt*)
Rare winter visitor.

10 records (3 reports, Whitaker, 19th century; 7 reports, 1950–72 TVBW).

The possibility of escaped birds or ferruginous-type hybrids has to be taken into account, especially in summer and spring. The period of wintering by vagrants can be from October to April.

Goldeneye *Bucephala clangula* (*Linnaeus*)
Generally has been a scarce winter visitor, but status upgraded to uncommon since 1968.

Because of its liking for coastal waters the goldeneye does not come inland in big numbers, although there is some increase when arctic conditions prevail. Those in Nottinghamshire can be found on all kinds of waters. It has taken to the gravel pits and yet is equally at home on old-established lakes.

The maximum present in any month of open weather is usually under 20 birds only exceeded by hard-weather influxes (eg 80 during the severe winter of 1947) until recently, when the normal population has risen to between 20 and 30. This is due to an increase in birdwatchers and an increase in waters (mainly gravel pits); and, possibly, to some increase in goldeneye.

Arrival and departure times are, in the main, very consistent, the first birds of the autumn appearing in October (usually the second half of the month) and the last leaving in April (often during the fourth week). Extreme dates are 30 September as the earliest for the autumn and 23 May as the latest for spring.

There are four peculiar dates: 19 June 1950, 30 June 1956, 30 June 1960 and 21 August 1955, which could be of escaped birds or of individuals which did not migrate and were leading a wandering existence.

Long-tailed duck   Clangula hyemalis (Linnaeus)
Rare passage migrant and winter visitor.

13 records (2, Whitaker; 11, TVBW).

Although rare, this marine duck is frequent enough to be discussed. If stormbound or bemused by fog during the autumn, it may appear on any water. Severe wintry conditions, such as in 1947, brings birds to the River Trent where, incidentally, both Whitaker's birds were taken. Finally, there is one spring record of a rather confiding bird which turned up on the Wollaton Park Lake.

Inclusive dates are 2 November to 11 February with 18 April isolated.

Velvet scoter   Melanitta fusca (Linnaeus)
Rare winter visitor.

5 records, 1880s, 1907, 1947, 1957, 1973.

Common scoter   Melanitta nigra (Linnaeus)
Scarce passage migrant.

Whitaker reported that this sea-duck occasionally appeared on the River Trent, mentioning one which was shot at Wilford, and then he listed 6 records for lakes in Central Nottinghamshire, which almost certainly portrays locality bias. The 85 records from 1942 to 1970 showed 63 at gravel pits, 13 on rivers, 3 at reservoirs, 2 for lakes and 1 each for sewage farm, flash and flood-water. As 88% were in the Trent Valley, the change of locality bias could be used again in reverse; nevertheless, the common scoter uses the Trent Valley considerably on its journeys north-east or south-west according to the time of year and the weather.

It has been seen in every month of the year, with April and August the most frequent months. It is a species associated with easterly winds.

Eider   Somateria mollissima (Linnaeus)
Rare vagrant.

1 shot, Nottingham floods, December 1878 or 1880 (Whitaker); a party of 16, December 1972, rose to 18, January 1973.

Ruddy duck   Oxyura jamaicensis (Gmelin)
Rare visitor.

Now feral in Britain. Recorded in Nottinghamshire in 1962 and 1963, probably birds from a Staffordshire colony.

Red-breasted merganser   Mergus serrator Linnaeus
Rare winter visitor, irregular.

The few appearances of this sawbill show very little pattern except for the following general details: 1, autumn birds can be expected on any water; 2, individuals have been recorded attached to the Dukeries goosander winter group; 3, hard-weather birds usually keep to the River Trent and nearby waters; 4, spring migrants behave similarly to the autumn birds. October to April.

Goosander   Mergus merganser Linnaeus

Uncommon winter visitor. Still regular in Dukeries, but fewer. Decrease has been offset to some extent by more regular appearances in Trent Valley.

Since 1942 the earliest arrival date in the autumn was 23 September. There were 2 October dates, but the first birds usually appear November or December. Last dates range from late February to 26 May but, depending on the weather of early spring, the normal goosander departure is during March or April.

Smew   Mergus albellus Linnaeus

Rare winter visitor generally.

Larger numbers occasionally appear, especially in severe winters, when the River Trent is used. At other times birds, usually brownheads, have been recorded on our lakes and other waters, especially the gravel pits.

Records from 1942 give the first birds in November on 3 occasions with the earliest on 5 November. December had the first birds for 11 of the years. January and February ranked as the main months for the smew in Nottinghamshire. Departure was delayed into March for 9 of the years and exceptionally into April: on 3 occasions with 10 April as the last date. In 1969 a female was seen on 21 June.

Shelduck   Tadorna tadorna (Linnaeus)

Rare summer visitor. Scarce/uncommon passage migrant.

Sterland mentioned that he had heard of this species breeding near the River Idle, but as it was hearsay, Whitaker did not repeat it. It could have been true because the shelduck at times has bred along the Trent Valley from the lower reaches up to close to Nottingham during TVBW times. Since the end of the old-style sewage farm none have been close to Nottingham and breeding has been confined to the stretch north of Newark. Recorded breeding from 1921.

The many movements and visitations show that this species occurs widely, to rest or stay on any type of water. Flooded land of the lower Idle and Trent Valleys is often visited, probably by birds from the Humber.

Records through the year are connected with the following groups:

1. Our small breeding stock which usually arrive in March and, if breeding is successful, are present till July or August.

2. Moult migration to the Heligoland Bight is most often apparent from July to October and birds of this group usually provide the largest numbers, up to 35 in a flock.

3. Passage of northern birds which travel south-west in the autumn and during hard weather, and north-east in the spring.

4. Idlers, which probably come in from the east coast.

Ruddy shelduck   Tadorna ferruginea (Pallas)
Rare visitor.

2, wild birds, 1869, Newstead Abbey, were probably genuine vagrants from the Mediterranean. Those recorded 1943, 1944 and 1973 could have been escaped birds.

Egyptian goose   Alopochen aegyptiacus (Linnaeus)
Feral in England, especially East Anglia.

Appearances in Nottinghamshire could be birds from East Anglia. Has attempted to breed.

Grey lag goose   Anser anser (Linnaeus)
Scarce winter visitor, irregular. Feral resident and visitor.

Has always been rare to scarce and of irregular appearance in Nottinghamshire, which lacks the correct habitat for the wary grey geese, although hedgerow disappearance is producing some extensive open areas which may be exploited one day, especially in the northern parts within easy distance of the Humber sanctuary. The grey lag is really a passage migrant which has settled for a winter visit if allowed, eg Whitaker mentioned a small flock which came to Walling Wells in September and stayed until well into the following spring for several years in the 1870s. During the 1940s a small party seemed regular at the year-end in the

Page 119 (above) Waxwing; (below) chaffinch at nest

Trent Valley on or close to the Nottingham Sewage Farm. In recent years, from 1964, more feral birds have been seen which often consort with the Canada goose flocks, and these visitors, perhaps from one of the nearby counties, tend to obscure the presence of the truly wild stock. Feral grey lag pairs were proved breeding in Nottinghamshire in 1971.

White-fronted goose   Anser albifrons (Scopoli)
Scarce/rare winter visitor and passage migrant, most years.

During Whitaker's time was a rare visitor, mainly to the Trent Valley and—people were handy with their guns in those days— his list of birds is very small.

From 1942, TVBW recording has gradually shown that this species is regular as a high-flying passage migrant and, from the skeins, tired birds occasionally come down to rest at some quiet or suitable spot. Naturally the Nottingham Sewage Farm attracted some, as also have the larger gravel-pit areas which combine grazing and safe harbourage. Flooded land in the Idle Valley has also been visited. During the very severe weather of early 1963 a flock of 21 settled in the Trent Valley from 19 January until 23 February, using the comparatively snow-free pastures from Colwick to Bulcote.

Has been recorded as early as 12 October and as late as 2 April.

Bean goose   Anser fabalis fabalis (Latham)
Rare winter visitor.

2 records, 1891 and later, around 1900 (Whitaker).

Pink-footed goose   Anser fabalis brachyrhynchus Baillon
Uncommon winter visitor. Occasional feral birds since 1962 at least.

Most surprisingly, Whitaker could only produce 2 records for his many years of recording during the 19th century to 1908, whereas since 1942 it has proved to be the most numerous of the grey geese which visit Nottinghamshire. As with the white-fronted, most are passage migrants in flight over the county, individuals and small groups coming to ground when tired. Gravel pits, floodwater and river-valley pasture have been visited.

Occasional feral birds now appear, presumably escapes from collections or released birds, which may follow the example of the feral grey lag and begin to breed using similar habitats to those of the Canada goose.

The earliest date for the wild pink-footed is 10 September and birds have been recorded for every month of autumn and winter until March. Latest date 16 March.

Snow goose   Anser caerulescens (Linnaeus)
The few Nottinghamshire reports are considered to concern escaped birds.

Brent goose   Branta bernicla (Linnaeus)
Rare vagrant.

5 records 1840s, 1850, 1889, 1956, 1957, 1973. The particular race was not always given, but the TVBW records were of the dark-breasted race. Wildfowlers have released some birds of this species within the country in recent years.

Barnacle goose   Branta leucopsis (Bechstein)
Rare vagrant.

8 records, 1869 (party of 52), 1890, late 19th century, 1956, 1963, 1967, 1969, 1970, 1973.

Possibly the 1970 bird and also other recent individuals were released by wildfowlers.

Canada goose   Branta canadensis (Linnaeus)
Feral, locally fairly common resident.

Some local movement to and from Derbyshire and Yorkshire, and some individuals have been connected with the moult migration to Scotland.

Whitaker gave no dates but did mention that it was breeding beside our lakes, presumably those of the Dukeries, where a recorded herd of 60 could have been the nucleus of present-day birds. Canada geese disperse widely for breeding on our waters, including Flintham, Kirklington, Newstead, Trent Valley gravel pits, Idle Valley waters and, formerly, at Kingston. After the breeding season, most return to the Dukeries 'lake district' where they join the residents to form a large herd for the winter. Whitaker's herd of 60 has grown to 450–500.

Mute swan   Cygnus olor (Gmelin)
Fairly common resident.

A census of the mute swan in 1955 discovered over 276 birds, made up of c 70 breeding pairs and 136 non-breeding birds. There were at least 90 cygnets also. Birds were breeding beside lakes, canals, gravel pits, ponds, marsh waters, rivers and streams. Apart from minor variations the population has remained constant with, possibly, some decrease by 1970. This could be due to the decline of the Trent Bridge herd of non-breeding birds which averaged c 80 in 1959 with a peak of 126 and then a decrease to an average of 4 during the winter 1969–70. The mute swan is also sensitive to water pollution, especially oil.

The colour variant, the so-called 'Polish swan', in which the cygnets are white from the beginning and the adults have certain colour variations, has occurred on a few occasions.

As with the Canada goose, the mute swan can be mistakenly thought of as sedentary, whereas there is a fairly constant turnover, new birds coming from other areas such as Lincolnshire and the south Midlands.

Whooper swan   Cygnus cygnus (Linnaeus)
Scarce winter visitor, most years.

To Whitaker its visitations were subject to weather and more were present during severe winters. TVBW records reveal an autumn appearance when, presumably, birds are entering Britain, and in the main they deal with random winter movements. Marsh waters, rivers, gravel pits and lakes are visited.

Nottinghamshire lies just south of the wintering range for the whooper swan, and consequently its visits show irregularity. The earliest autumn date is 16 October, all other first dates being in either November or December. March is the normal departure month but some years stragglers stay into April. A very late date was 24 May in 1959.

In 1949 an adult bird spent the summer from July to October at Welbeck.

Bewick's swan   Cygnus bewickii Yarrell
Now a regular and generally uncommon winter visitor.

Every year now birds frequent the valleys of the Idle and the Trent, preferring an area holding water for refuge, and grassland for grazing. Floodwater always attracts and gravel pits are frequently used. Other tired migrants are likely to turn up anywhere, such as on lakes and reservoirs.

Whitaker considered the Bewick's swan to be very rare, and yet he listed a herd of 60 (1899) and a herd of 21 (1902). TVBW records reveal a radical change. From 1942 to 1949 it was a rare and only occasional winter visitor (5 reports totalling 21 birds); from 1950 it was recorded annually, beginning with single birds for 1950 and 1951 followed by 4 reports for 36 birds to 1954; from 1955 the number of records and the total number of birds have increased, with herds of 50–60 appearing; and since 1962 this swan has been fairly common at times. Sometimes well over 100 have lived in the county.

The earliest autumn arrival date has been 20 October (in 1968). The pattern for all the other 20 years is for the early arrivals to appear in November, and the main arrival and movement to take place during December. Numbers are variable for January and February according to the weather and feeding areas.

Return arrivals and north-east movement are from late February and into March. Stragglers are fairly frequent into April. The last, isolated, date is 12 May.

Buzzard   Buteo buteo (Linnaeus)
Scarce vagrant.

Bred 1820s, became scarcer (and rare, seemingly, by the 1870s).

Was a scarce resident 1955-8 (following myxomatosis) but breeding not proved.

Truly vagrant, this species has been seen in every month of the year. From the 1960s large importations of raptors from India and elsewhere have added confusion due to sightings of the all too frequent escaped birds. However, excluding the years when the buzzard was resident, the pattern of arrival and departure shows a wintering period from August to April—remembering, of course, that some of the autumn and spring birds are passage migrants. When easterly winds persist during the spring, buzzards occur during May and June.

Rough-legged buzzard   Buteo lagopus (Pontoppidan)
Rare vagrant.
   12 reports, 1857–1915, 1926, 1968.

Red-tailed hawk   Buteo jamaicensis borealis
Rare vagrant.
   1 shot, autumn 1850 (Whitaker). In view of recently acquired knowledge of trans-Atlantic crossings, this record is considered to be a good one, but it remains unacceptable by the BOU until the specimen can be found.

Sparrowhawk   Accipter nisus (Linnaeus)
Scarce resident.
   Whitaker thought this species was thinly distributed and more plentiful about the forest. The TVBW have found it to be a scarce resident which became rare during the toxic seed-dressings years. By 1970 more were present, but nowhere numerous.

Goshawk   Accipter gentilis (Linnaeus)
Rare vagrant.
   4 records (1848, one undated, Whitaker; 1945, 1947, TVBW).

Red kite   Milvus milvus (Linnaeus)
Rare vagrant.
7 records (3 reports, 1 undated, 1847, 1860, Whitaker; 4 reports, 1947, 1967, 1972 (2) TVBW). Formerly resident.

White-tailed eagle   Haliaeetus albicilla (Linnaeus)
Rare vagrant.
3 records, 1838, 1857, 1896.

Honey buzzard   Pernis apivorus (Linnaeus)
Rare summer visitor/passage migrant.
Of the 140 or so years covered by this review, this species has been recorded during 23–24 summers when, at times, it has bred, attempted to breed or been suspected of breeding.

Marsh harrier   Circus aeruginosus (Linnaeus)
Rare vagrant or passage migrant.
10 records, 1848, 1945, 1953, 1959, 1966, 1969, 1971, 1972.
Usually seen in spring, sometimes in summer, a little more frequently in autumn—August–September. Movement, at times, is part of the migrational flow by Continental birds. 1 winter appearance, January 1945.

Hen harrier   Circus cyaneus (Linnaeus)
Rare winter visitor.
The commonest of the 3 harrier species which visit Nottinghamshire. 24 records at least.
Earliest birds appear in September and, from then on, this species can be seen as a passage bird or winter visitor until March. April and May birds are considered to be passage migrants.

Montagu's harrier   Circus pygargus (Linnaeus)
Rare passage migrant.
7 reports (1884, 1905, Whitaker; five reports, 1944, 1945, 1953, 1969, 1972, TVBW), also a pair were present, summers of 1955 and 1956.

Most of the few birds recorded have been from June to July. The earliest for this species was 2 April in 1844, and the latest, 23 October in 1945

Harrier sp

From 20 reports, 1942–73, of unidentified harriers, the following were almost certain:

Marsh harrier: 1964, 1968, 1970
Hen harrier: 1946, 1949, 1958, 1968, 1970, 1973
Montagu's harrier: 1950, 1968

The rest were 'ringtails'.

Osprey   Pandion haliaetus (Linnaeus)

Rare passage migrant.

Around 32 reports (11, Whitaker; 1, Whitlock; c 20, TVBW).

Migrating birds seek out any water containing fish and the osprey has now occurred quite widely in Nottinghamshire. Some were seen following the course of the River Trent.

The return of this species to Scotland is probably the reason for an increase in local records as shown by the following summary (birds seen):

1939–1905 (66 years)   12
1906–64   (59 years)   7
1965–73   (9 years)   13

Spring passage has occurred from 17 April to 31 May; autumn from 26 August to 5 October. Whitaker gave no precise dates for his records.

Hobby   Falco subbuteo Linnaeus

Rare vagrant and summer visitor.

Has occurred more frequently since 1965. Over 29 records (over 16 reports, Whitaker; at least 13, TVBW). Suspected of having bred or attempted to breed, but not proved.

Most reports are for the months of June, July and August. Whitaker cited 4 late birds, 1 in November and 3 in December.

Peregrine   Falco peregrinus Tunstall
Rare winter visitor and passage migrant. Irregular.

No records for May and June. 3 reports for July–August, and then an increase from September to December. Most occurrences in January. Departure and passage noted during March and April. Inclusive dates for the above are 2 July to 24 April.

In recent times there has been a number of escaped falcons, such as the lanner and the saker, and all falcons should be scrutinised most carefully.

Merlin   Falco columbarius Linnaeus
Rare winter visitor and passage migrant.

First arrivals after the breeding season have been from July (1 record), August (2 records), and then many records for September to December. After the January–February wintering reports there have been 6 reports from March to May, latest date 10 May.

Red-footed falcon   Falco vespertinus Linnaeus
1 in 1973.

Kestrel   Falco tinnunculus Linnaeus
Fairly common resident. Fairly common/common out of the breeding season, most in early autumn.

The local assessment from about 1850 to 1970 is of a generally distributed species much subject to persecution from egg-collectors or from keepers of game birds or, more recently, from novice 'falconers'. Fortunately, some people have always recognised the usefulness and the beauty, both in line and movement, of this bird and have protected it according to the law.

No surveys have been carried out on the kestrel in Nottinghamshire, where it has been generally looked upon as common, although this status includes autumn and winter when the county receives birds from elsewhere.

A study of *The Population Density of the Kestrel in Leicestershire* was carried out in 1963 and 1964 by members of the Leicestershire

& Rutland Ornithological Society (M. E. Griffiths, 1967), when a density of 1 pair to about 3,500 acres (c5½ square miles) on mixed farmland was obtained. The author thought that an increase in cultivation could affect the numbers of kestrels by reducing the number of small mammals and, consequently, fewer kestrels may be expected in arable than in rough grassland districts. This has some bearing upon an assessment of the kestrel in Nottinghamshire, in view of similar farming habitats, provided it is borne in mind that our arable land since 1958 has always been more than twice that under grass, and it is possible that the kestrel population is less dense in Nottinghamshire than in Leicestershire and Rutland.

Following the use of toxic seed-dressings (chlorinated hydrocarbon BHC types), the kestrel became quite rare as a breeding bird in Nottinghamshire, which led to more interest being taken in it by the TVBW. Improvement in numbers was noticeable following the voluntary ban on the toxic seed-dressings and, when reported nests or breeding pairs were plotted on a map, density was approximately 1 pair to 3,840 acres (6 square miles) in some areas and 1 pair to 3,840–6,400 acres (6–10 square miles) in the majority of areas. North-east Notts was poorly covered due to a lack of observers. This assessment is only a rough guide and a serious survey would almost certainly discover more breeding kestrels.

Passage migrants and winter visitors appear as some of our own birds move south and, as it is impossible to differentiate between the groups, the summary of August and September for arrival, passage and dispersal, and March to April for return and for northward movement, can only be of a general nature. Birds during May and June can be safely assumed to belong to Nottinghamshire's own breeding stock.

Red grouse   Lagopus lagopus scoticus (Latham)
Rare vagrant.
   6 records, 1860, 1863, 1883, 1903, one undated, and 1941.
   Visits by this moorland species are purely accidental. The birds

of 1860, 1863 and 1883 were thought to have come from the Derbyshire moors because of severe weather. The 1941 record has a wartime connection: it is thought a heavy air-raid or Sheffield caused the birds to flee.

Black grouse   Lyrurus tetrix britannicus (Witherby)
A lost species no longer present.

Formerly a fairly common, but local resident—'packs of fifty were seen'. By 1877 was breeding sparingly, and became rare by the end of the 19th century. Late dates: single birds shot, 1910, 1915, 1917.

Red-legged partridge   Alectoris rufa (Linnaeus)
First authenticated occurrence, 1851. Several pairs turned loose, 1872, Clipstone. Now a fairly common resident.

This species is widespread and evidence points to 1–2 pairs per 100 acres. The red-legged seems to be standing up well to the various pressures, and the reduction of animal food because of sprays has perhaps been less troublesome to this species since it feeds on aphids, seeds and other vegetable matter at the sides of the intensively cultivated crops (Potts, 1970).

Partridge   Perdix perdix (Linnaeus)
Still a common resident, but a decrease in numbers under modern farming conditions.

Record bag, October 1906, 752 brace shot by 8 guns (Whitaker). At times, local stock has been supplemented by Hungarian birds.

The report which came from the late L. Key and the late W. Priestley on the status of the common partridge for a 1,000 acre estate in south Nottinghamshire typifies the decline of this species since the 1950s. At first the observers reported a happy state of affairs (L. Key as keeper, knew the partridge situation well). Later, a change of ownership saw a dramatic change in land usage. What was predominantly grassland was ploughed up and the area became mainly arable with corn as the main crop. Hedgerows were grubbed up, farm-machine traffic trebled, and spraying increased.

The partridge population suffered from a reduction of safe nest sites and from a diminished insect-food supply for the chicks. Importations of partridges from elsewhere failed to halt the decline. During the 1960s the shooting syndicate terminated their lease, L. Key moved away, and our news of these south Nottinghamshire partridges came to an end.

On an estate in north Nottinghamshire there were 227 pairs and 10 singles on 1,492 acres in 1963, even though the preceding winter was extremely harsh. This is approximately 15 pairs to 100 acres and reflects suitable wild habitat, careful husbandry by keepers, and a shooting interest.

On the survey farms where the birds have to shift for themselves entirely, the average was around 3 pairs to the 100 acres during the 1960s, a dismal comparison made worse when it is realised that sometimes there was no breeding.

Quail *Coturnix coturnix (Linnaeus)*
Rare summer visitor, irregular.

This small game bird probably comes to Nottinghamshire every year and breeds, although there are years when it is not recorded, usually a failure in observation rather than lack of birds. There is not much information on numbers, apart from knowing that periodically there are 'Quail Years', when more are located; in these years, such as in 1964 when 9 males were in 6 areas, numbers are recorded. Distribution is widespread, most reports coming from the lighter land. Whitaker considered it scarce and rarer than formerly which, taking into account knowledge of this species since 1935, suggests that there has been little change in the last 80 years.

Earliest recorded arrival date is 17 May. Main arrival is from 20 May to 4 June. As small young have been seen well into August, departure must take place during September with stragglers into October. Exceptional late dates are 7 November (TVBW) and December (shot, Whitaker).

Pheasant   Phaiuanus colchicus Linnaeus
Common resident.

Because of hand-rearing it is difficult to assess the density of this species on farmland, but wild birds, 'unsullied' by man's dole, are widespread and, perhaps, at a density of a pair or two per 100 acres. Numbers are variable in woodland depending on whether or not game is preserved for shooting.

Crane   Grus grus (Linnaeus)
Rare vagrant.

3 records, 1, 1851 (Wollaton Hall Museum); 1, 1875 (Whitaker); 1, 1968 (TVBW).

Water rail   Rallus aquaticus Linnaeus
Rare summer resident. First authenticated breeding, 1971. Uncommon winter visitor.

Because of its skilful skulking this species is not readily observed. It has been recorded widely in our wet places, being regular among patches of sedge, rush and willow at the ends of lakes, dams and old gravel pits. Others have been seen near rivers, beside quiet streams and in wet willow holts. Sometimes a total of 30 birds has been recorded during the winter from the few main areas visited by TVBW members but, as there are numerous suitable places throughout the county, the wintering population must be considerably more. Breeding has long been suspected and was successfully proved recently, although numbers are still considered to be small.

Earliest autumn arrivals occur during July (earliest date, 16th), but general first arrival is during August and September. Influxes take place later at times. General departure is during March and April.

Spotted crake   Porzana porzana (Linnaeus)
Rare passage migrant.

Considered must have bred, Nottingham marshes, around 1871 (Whitaker).

Of the 3 Porzana crake species, the spotted occurs the most frequently in Nottinghamshire. Apart from the occasional wintering bird, the records fall into the migration periods of 1 March to 18 April and 1 August to 25 September.

Baillon's crake   Porzana pusilla (Pallas)
Rare vagrant.
   4 records, 1893, 1 shortly after, 1921, 1922.

Little crake   Porzana parva (Scopoli)
Rare vagrant.
   1 in 1970.

Corncrake   Crex crex (Linnaeus)
Rare summer visitor and passage migrant. Irregular.
   Whitaker wrote in 1907 that 'twenty years back it was the exception in the spring not to hear a corncrake in nearly every mowing field in the Trent Valley, and almost every seed and grass field left for hay in other parts. In this high and dry valley [Blidworth] we had from ten to fifteen pairs, now for the last three years not a bird has been heard.'
   Records from other sources reveal a continued decline and from being said to be common from 1912–14 the corncrake was generally lost as a breeding species from 1935. From 1950–70 records show that it attempted to breed twice and was present throughout the breeding season on two other occasions at least. This sad disappearance was generally blamed on the increased use of farm machinery in the hayfields which resulted in the killing of the sitting females and the destruction of eggs and young.
   Whitaker's first dates when this species was a regular summer visitor were from 24 April to 15 May for 32 of the years 1871–1906. As a passage migrant, TVBW records show 23 April to late May for northward movement, and 3 August to 27 September for southward movement. Most migrants of the autumn appear in September. Late birds were recorded twice in October, and there is 1 report of a bird wintering from December 1953 to January 1954.

Moorhen   Gallinula chloropus (Linnaeus)
Common resident.

Coot   Fulica atra Linnaeus
Common resident.

Requiring a larger area of water than the moorhen, the coot is found everywhere, ranging from 1 or 2 pairs on small waters such as the Oxton Bogs to many pairs where there are sufficient suitable places for nests. The development of the wet gravel pits created more breeding areas and must have more than doubled the breeding population. In 1957, 230 pairs were present for 37 areas of Nottinghamshire. This total has been passed, due to the run of mildish winters from 1963 as much as to increased acreage of habitat, and 2 areas alone in 1970, the flooded Carrlands (a temporary breeding area) and the Attenborough Nature Reserve, held a total of c 452 adults from May to July.

The winter population has shown a similar increase since 1963 with c 3,000 being present by the early 1970s (2,867 were counted in 20 areas).

Evidence of immigration from Europe is not forthcoming. There is a dispersal from the breeding waters and there is a build-up in numbers during the autumn. Hard weather causes movement and also concentrations in the Trent Valley.

Great bustard   Otis tarda Linnaeus
Rare vagrant.
    1 in 1906.

Little bustard   Otis tetrax Linnaeus
Rare vagrant.
    4 or 5 records: (1) 1854, (1) 1856, (2) 1883, (1) 1906. All Whitaker, but the 1 for 1889 was not mentioned in his *Notes on the Birds of Nottinghamshire,* 1907.

Oystercatcher   Haematopus ostralegus Linnaeus
Rare passage migrant and vagrant, most years, usually single birds.

Attempted breeding 1969, eggs taken or young failed.

The spring passage normally begins about the third week of March, although individuals have moved through as early as mid-February. Passage continues into early June, with late April to the end of May being the peak period when 3–4 birds have been noted on occasions.

The first week of August usually marks the start of the autumn passage, although 18 July is the earliest date. The main passage is from mid-August to mid-September. Nocturnal movement has been noted on occasions, but no evidence of flock size has been obtained. This movement extends to the last week of September apart from an exceptionally late record of 27 October. Occasionally appear in winter.

Lapwing Vanellus vanellus (Linnaeus)
Common resident, but reduction on farmland 1960 onwards.

Abundant autumn, but variable numbers winter. Whitaker, for the period from the late 19th century into the first decade of the 20th century, reported this species as breeding in fairly large numbers all over the cultivated parts. The Editor, in his energetic cycling youth during the 1930s, knew it as a common species especially on the pastures. Since World War II, a county-wide drainage policy, considerable loss of grassland to arable and, on the arable, disturbance by farm machinery plus reduction of insect food from spraying, have combined against the lapwing and reduced breeding numbers have been noticeable for the last 10 or more years. Density in many areas is less than 1 pair per 200 acres.

The departure of the Continental lapwings usually takes place during March, and by the end of this month our fields are left to the resident breeding population.

From early June small parties of adults and immatures begin to move across the county in south-westerly/westerly directions and, at the same time, there is a build-up of local flocks which can, by early August, be of a maximum of 1,000, although 100–200 birds per flock is average. During autumn the build-up accelerates with the big arrival of Continental birds, which sees a peak in October, or often during November and December.

Severe weather sets in motion an exodus to the south-west and west. In really hard weather, as in 1947 and 1963, there is a complete departure. A return movement takes place as soon as the weather is favourable.

Ringed plover *Charadrius hiaticula Linnaeus*
Fairly common passage migrant.

Attempted breeding 1966, 1972 and 1973.

The spring passage may begin in the first week of March, but normally towards the end of this month; in some years this species is not recorded until late April or even May, but this may be due to scarcity of birdwatchers rather than birds. Movement is most evident during the second half of May, when peak numbers are noted. Numbers decrease from early June with occasional birds up to the middle of the month, exceptionally into the third week.

The return southward movement takes place from mid-June, although passage is not definite until July and then usually in the second half of the month. Passage from then on is steady, with a peak from mid-August into the first week of September. The highest number observed on any one day stands at 90, recorded on 20 September 1947; heavy numbers occurred in the early autumn of that year.

From mid-September numbers decline until, by the end of October, most birds have gone; occasional birds may linger into mid-November. Infrequently, the ringed plover will be seen in winter, thought to be drifting to the south-west to milder conditions.

Little ringed plover *Charadrius dubius Scopoli*
Scarce summer visitor and passage migrant.

The first pair was proved to breed in 1956, and 39 pairs were present in 1970–71.

The earliest bird back from winter quarters was from 10 February in 1961. The last week of March to early April usually marks the start of arrival and through movement. Passage and consolidation continues into May, ending during the first week of June, but some of these late birds could be seeking a suitable nesting territory and their movement need not be true migration.

The local breeding birds and independent birds of the year gather at suitable feeding areas, making the start of the southward migration difficult to detect. The first week of July seems to mark the beginning and it continues into August, with peaks at times. By the end of August or the first week of September there is an obvious decrease, with only single birds being recorded, the latest date is 28 October.

Kentish plover   Charadrius alexandrinus Linnaeus
Rare passage migrant/vagrant.
   5 records, 1804, 1947, 1950, 1952, 1959.

Grey plover   Pluvialis squatarola (Linnaeus)
Scarce/rare passage migrant. Most years.
   The inclusive dates for the spring passage are 8 April–6 June, the first half of May being the peak passage period. Autumn movement has been noted as early as August and birds may occur at any time from then until mid-November, with the second half of September the peak period. Birds have occurred during the winter. Normal sightings are of 1–2 birds, groups of up to 10 occasionally.

Golden plover   Pluvialis apricaria apricaria (Linnaeus) and *P. a. altifrons Brehm*
Passage migrant and winter visitor.
   Late autumn and early spring gatherings not so large during the last decade (1960–70), perhaps due to loss of pasture. At the end of winter there is a general build-up and Nottinghamshire may be one of their traditional gathering areas. March and April mark this time when the birds of the northern race show off their breeding finery. By the third week of April most have gone, leaving only very occasional flocks into May. Latest date 9 June.

I

There are two arrival movements, first the southern race and later birds of the northern race. The two may merge. The first birds and occasional flock of the autumn passage occur from the second week of July onwards (earliest 27 June), although most years the first birds appear at the end of July and during early August. From then on there is a steady increase with flocks of 100 or more being sighted. Later in the autumn, usually in November, the main peak is reached, when flocks of 1,000 or more have been observed. Severe frosts or snow will force the birds to depart.

Dotterel   Eudromias morinellus (Linnaeus)
Rare passage migrant.

14 records at least (some 6 reports, 1859–1901, Whitaker; recorded at Besthorpe, Oates; 7 reports, 1924–73, TVBW).

Sightings were on 3 spring dates—late April, 2 May and just May, and in the autumn on 6 dates between 16 August and 29 September.

Turnstone   Arenaria interpres (Linnaeus)
Scarce passage migrant.

Exceptionally early birds have appeared in April (earliest, 19 April), but usual passage is from the first week of May continuing occasionally into early June (latest, 7 June). 1 or 2 birds are normally recorded, sometimes up to 5, with 8 on 2 occasions.

In the autumn, passage birds have been as early as 12 July, although the first birds usually appear towards the end of July or early August. In 1944 this species appeared in above average numbers, the highest total for 1 day being 18 with up to 9 for several days. Most years the southerly movement may continue throughout August, and sometimes into September, but rarely into October. Latest recorded date 16 November.

Snipe   Gallinago gallinago (Linnaeus)
Fairly common up to 1930–40, now an uncommon resident due to loss of breeding habitat.

Common winter visitor and passage migrant.

During March and April a general northward movement becomes evident as birds head back to their breeding grounds and, by early May, almost all have left Nottinghamshire.

Snipe reappear in small numbers from early July (earliest bird of passage, 3 July) and there is a trickle until early August when numbers steadily increase and sometimes reach a peak of 100 by the end of the month. Passage continues throughout September into October, with usually several peaks. By November gatherings of up to 200 may occur at wet places if these are made available by flooding. Numbers level out by mid-December with scattered small groups the rule, plus a gathering of 100 here and there. Hard weather causes considerable departure.

Great snipe   Gallinago media (Latham)
Rare passage migrant and winter visitor.

9 records, 1882, 1883, 1910, 1913, Whitaker; 1947, 1952, 1968, 1971, 1973, TVBW.

Jack snipe   Lymnocryptes minima (Brünnich)
Scarce passage migrant and winter visitor.

Maximum gathering, 27 birds (1971).

An exceptionally early date was 23 August. Normal early movement is from mid-September with the main passage during October.

The small winter stock is augmented by other birds during March as the spring migration builds up and this northward passage continues into April. Stragglers may linger until the second week of May; latest record was 1 June.

Woodcock   Scolopax rusticola Linnaeus
Uncommon resident and winter visitor.

Whitaker did not consider Nottinghamshire a good woodcock county. He mentioned a certain winter shoot at Thieves Wood (then of birch and oak) and the bag of 36 constituted a record. He also mentioned that this species delighted to be in conifer plantations when the trees were between 10–20 years old, but this was long before the Forestry Commission began.

TVBW findings reveal that it is widespread as a breeding species, with the forest country its stronghold. There are far more woodcock breeding in the county nowadays than there are snipe. Some of these breeding birds are associated with conifers, but contrary to what Whitaker stated, it is feared that the loss of hardwoods on the Keuper Marl could cause a decrease there.

Because of our own resident stock, movements are not easy to tabulate. Migration is often detected by the appearance of a bird in an unusual and unlikely place, such as the city centre or even a suburban garden! Some Dukeries keepers consider that the Nottinghamshire woodcock move away after breeding and their places are taken by Continental birds which arrive during the autumn. Certainly the bags obtained by shooters in habitats where local stock is not plentiful demonstrate a good arrival from elsewhere. There is too little evidence to allow discussion on spring movement.

Curlew Numenius arquata (Linnaeus)
Scarce resident. Common passage migrant, 20th century, until modernisation of the Nottingham Sewage Farm 1962–3. Now uncommon passage migrant and winter visitor.

Whitaker does not record this species as ever breeding and it seems to have begun to nest with us during the 20th century. TVBW records mention it as a probable breeding species in 1945 but, considering the limitations to mobility in those times, it probably means that local ornithologists were a little late in the discovery. This may have been by only a few years, judging by the findings for the country as a whole (Parslow, 1967), when the spread to the lowlands was considered to have been in the late 1930s.

Numbers in Nottinghamshire have always been small with a maximum of 14 pairs breeding, using grassland mainly but occasionally arable. The adverse conditions inhibiting the lapwing and the snipe must also affect the curlew. From 1960–70 up to 8 pairs have been found breeding and the valleys of the Soar, Trent and Idle have been favoured. Elsewhere breeding has been sporadic.

A scrutiny of TVBW annual reports will show that different populations have been involved. Firstly, there is the small breeding stock, of which individuals can appear at their breeding sites during February when mild enough, usually the males taking up their stations in March. Just when these birds leave is not known, but departure is thought to be in July, and by August at latest.

The curlew eras must be explained:

1. The years of the old-style Nottingham Sewage Farm, that large artificial marsh which from 1920–5 until 1962 offered remarkable facilities for curlew, becoming the home of up to 250 birds from July to early April (see TVBW annual report for 1961 on the Wintering Flock of Curlews, East of Nottingham). This area was attractive to other populations of migrating curlews, and there were several waves during the long season of southward movements, with peaks in August and September and, occasionally, a later one in October. At such times when these highly vocal and restless birds thronged the area (often numbering 300 to 400) their calls resounded and echoed from the valley side at Burton Joyce.

2. Present times, when very few feeding areas exist and when the migrating curlew is something of a rarity. In 1970, we have a small number of spring reports for the movement of this large wader and much reduced observation during the autumn. First birds can turn up as early as 20 June, but usually migration does not get underway until late July and, as mentioned above, peak movement time is from mid-August till just after mid-September. A Nottinghamshire watcher of the 1970s, unless the conservation movement can obtain or create some wetland habitat, will see this migration as a chance party moving south-westwards during the day, or will hear it as voices in the night, part of the great unseen nocturnal movement.

Winter numbers are now very small and of haphazard appearance and movement.

Whimbrel   Numenius phaeopus (Linnaeus)

Uncommon passage migrant.

Usually observed in small numbers in the county, this wader is seen on the ground only on rare occasions. There are times when good numbers are observed such as the several flocks of August 1944 which totalled c 200 birds.

Spring passage dates are from 8 April to 25 June.

In the autumn, birds have occurred as early as 10 July and, after the peak time of August into early September, migration has continued to 23 October.

Black-tailed godwit   Limosa limosa (Linnaeus)

Scarce passage migrant, most years.

In the spring birds may be seen between the first week of April and the fourth week of June. The majority of records are for the period 20 April to 12 May.

During the autumn passage this species may occur from the second week of July, earliest 8 July, and although appearances are sporadic and usually of smaller numbers, the second half of August is the time when most birds are noted. Passage continues throughout September with a few stragglers into October. Last recorded date 2 November.

Bar-tailed godwit   Limosa lapponica (Linnaeus)

Scarce passage migrant, most years. Very occasional winter visitor.

Never frequent or common, the bar-tailed godwit may be met with from the first week of April to the first week of June. 6 April is considered to be the earliest date and the record for 3 March 1963 is judged to concern a wintering bird. The earliest date for the autumn passage is 4 July, but normal first birds occur at the end of July or in early August. Birds have turned up even at the end of October.

Green sandpiper   Tringa ochropus Linnaeus

Fairly common passage migrant. Scarce winter visitor.

At the end of winter the presence of our few green sandpipers makes it difficult to assess when the spring migration begins. However, mid-March appears to be the time when a slight increase occurs and passage then continues into April, usually of ones and twos (but maximum 20), and there is a considerable falling off into May. Stragglers occur into the first half of June.

Sometimes there is an overlap between the last spring bird and the first autumn one, and birds in Nottinghamshire between 14 and 18 June can belong to either movement. Normal southward movement begins around 20 June, and numbers increase in July to a minor peak between 14 and 20 July. August always has a major wave but, in some years, this can be in two parts, with a rush of birds in early August then a pause, followed by another peak towards the end of the month. Weather cycles and winds can affect the timing of these peaks. After another peak in September there is a sharp decrease to small numbers in October.

Up to 5 birds may winter in Nottinghamshire from November onwards.

Wood sandpiper   Tringa glareola Linnaeus
Uncommon passage migrant.

This traveller over and through the county usually comes when the winds have a touch of east in them. Spring passage is very light and the inclusive period for its appearance is from 26 April to 9 June, when the usual first birds are seen during the second week of May. June birds are exceptional.

In 1961 a bird, possibly sick, stayed in the Trent Valley from 12 February to 16 July.

Birds of the autumn passage are more frequent and may be seen from 22 June onwards, although they normally begin moving through around mid-July. Numbers are usually small, 1–5 being the average at any one time. Sometimes minor peaks occur in August and September when up to 10 birds have been recorded, and in September 1958 there was a maximum of 25. Good years for the wood sandpiper occur infrequently and average out to about 1 in 5.

There is a marked decline at the end of September with only

occasional records into the first half of October. Late birds have been noted twice in November: the latest being 23 November.

Solitary sandpiper   Tringa solitaria Wilson
Rare vagrant.
    1 in 1962.

Common sandpiper   Actitis hypoleucos (Linnaeus)
Fairly common passage migrant. Very probably bred, 1973.
    The spring movement begins during the first week of April (earliest date, 31 March) and continues until the first half of June in some years. Numbers are fairly small usually, 1–5 being generally recorded in an area. Sometimes a peak of up to 10 is reached, mostly end of April to mid-May.
    Southward migration may begin as early as mid-June, ie some years the first of the autumn birds appears on a date which can bring the last of the spring birds in other years. Normally the very first birds occur towards the end of June. Passage is steady during July with peaks usually during August of up to 50–60 birds at times, daily average for the county is 10–20 birds. During September, movement slackens to 1–5 by the end of the month. Individuals may linger into the second half of October, or even November; latest date 29 November.
    There is 1 winter record of a bird in late December.

Spotted sandpiper   Actitis macularia (Linnaeus)
Rare vagrant. Whitaker records 1 shot, March 1848, Thoresby, but this record does not figure in the British List.

Redshank   Tringa totanus (Linnaeus)
Uncommon summer visitor since 1962, formerly fairly common. Scarce passage migrant and winter visitor.
    Whitaker gave 1884 as the earliest date he knew of the redshank nesting in our county, when Nottinghamshire came under the influence of this species as it spread inland as a breeding bird. By 1906 he was able to report it as breeding in considerable numbers

along the valleys of the Trent and the Idle. This happy state continued to the beginning of the 1960s.

In 1959 the TVBW carried out a census of breeding redshank and obtained the following results: the Idle watershed, 131 birds, 64–77 pairs; the Trent Valley, including tributaries such as the Leen and Dover Beck, 65 birds, 32–33 pairs; Vale of Belvoir, 4 birds, 2 pairs; Soar Valley, 4 birds, 2 pairs. Total, 204 birds, 100–113 pairs. At the time of this census the first effects of drainage and changes in land usage were discernible, suggesting that the population had been higher at one time. Maximum numbers may have lasted from the beginning of this century until the late 1950s, and the big decrease became apparent when there was no rapid recovery after the heavy losses during the 1962–3 winter.

Two movements take place at the end of winter: 1, the return of our breeding stock in strength from early March, and 2, the movement of passage migrants, 1–8 birds, during March and April, occasionally into early May.

Autumn passage may begin as early as the third week of June, but generally this southward migration begins in mid-July. Most of the local breeding birds leave or disperse at the end of July or during early August. Passage of this species is always steady in small numbers, most birds appearing August and September, the movement ending in October.

Numbers are small in winter and, in mild years such as since 1963, the wintering redshank are thought to be of our own breeding stock.

Spotted redshank   Tringa erythropus (Pallas)
Uncommon to scarce passage migrant in autumn, and rare and irregular in spring.

Most of the spring birds are seen mid-April to mid-May. In 1957 a bird set up territory in the Trent Valley from 22 March to 4 May, and what was thought to be the same individual reappeared 23–24 June.

Autumn movement is regular and the maximum has been 12 birds. A bird in late June or early July is exceptional, and normal first birds are reported from mid-July or early August. Movement is steady with sometimes a peak between the third week of August and mid-September. By the end of September almost all birds have passed through, the occasional straggler turning up in October. Latest record 24 November.

Lesser yellowlegs Tringa fiavipes (*Gmelin*)
Rare vagrant. 1 shot, 1854.

Greenshank Tringa nebularia (*Gunnerus*)
Fairly common passage migrant.

The spring passage may begin as early as 4 April. However, it is usually the last week of April or the first week of May. Passage, normally sparse, may continue until the first, rarely the second, week of June. Usually 1–2 birds are recorded at any one time, and the maximum is 7.

In autumn, birds may occur from the last week of June onwards, although the second half of July usually marks the start of general movement. Passage is steady throughout August and the first half of September, with parties of 1–5 birds normally and 10–20 at peak times. By the third week of September movement becomes very slack, with only 1–2 birds, and the end of this month often marks the end of the passage. In some years birds are recorded into October and exceptionally into November. In 1970 an individual stayed from 28 October to 20 December.

1946 provided the only winter record, probably involving 1 bird, observed on 10 January and 10 March.

Knot Calidris canutus (*Linnaeus*)
Scarce passage migrant. Rare and occasional winter visitor.

During the spring passage knot may be seen from mid-March to the first week of June with 1–3 the usual numbers.

The earliest autumn record is for 24 June but, most years, the first migrants are seen during the second half of July or the first half of August. Birds can be seen during September, occasionally into October and November, and in December on rare visits.

Winter appearances are usually of single birds, but a party of 8 were seen one year.

Purple sandpiper   Calidris maritima (Brünnich)
Rare passage migrant.

7 records, 1864, 1885, 1944, 1946, 1949, 1966, 1972.

Single birds have turned up on a few occasions and the dates from 9 August to 24 October show a connection with some kind of overland migration.

Little stint   Calidris minuta (Leisler)
Uncommon passage migrant, most years.

The earliest spring record is 9 March, but the second week of May is the time when the first migrants may occur. Passage is very light extending to mid-June at times.

During autumn passage more are seen, with up to 10 or more noted on occasions. The maximum is 40, recorded in 1946. This is another migrant associated with easterly winds, and records show 21 July as the earliest for the autumn. The first birds often arrive in early August and movement continues into September, with minor peaks in late August and during the second half of September. Reports to mid-October are uncommon. A late individual lingered from 13 November to 15 December in 1963.

Temminck's stint   Calidris temminckii (Leisler)
Rare passage migrant, irregular.

Of the 8 records, concerning 8–9 birds, noted during the spring, the inclusive dates of appearance are 1 May to 19 May.

During the autumn, when more have been observed, the inclusive dates are 26 July to 12 October, with August and September prominent for main passage. Normally 1–2 birds are observed but the maximum is 7 on 14 September 1946.

Pectoral sandpiper   Calidris melanotos (Veiillot)
Rare vagrant.

Four records, 1948, 1962, 1968, 1973.

There is 1 June record and 3 for September.

Dunlin   Calidris alpina (Linnaeus)

Common passage migrant. Uncommon out of passage seasons.

This ubiquitous little wader is regularly recorded in every month of the year. During the spring migration birds may be seen from the second week of March through to May and occasionally into the first half of June. Numbers are variable, usually 1–10, occasionally 15–30, sometimes up to 60.

Return movement may begin from the last week of June, although it is usually some time in July when the first migrants occur. Passage is normally steady throughout August and September, with occasional peaks of up to 20 and exceptionally numbers have topped 50. Totals of up to 200 were reported at the old-style Nottingham Sewage Farm. Passage slackens off and numbers become small during October, with few birds left by November.

During December to February further movement takes place during hard weather and also, if conditions are suitable, ie flooded land, flocks of static birds (60 or more) may be seen at times.

Curlew sandpiper   Calidris ferruginea (Pontoppidan)

Uncommon passage migrant, most years.

Since 1944 this species has only been recorded in 3 years during spring, all observed in May.

During autumn, numbers are variable and, without doubt, appearances are closely connected with weather systems over Russia and Europe as well as over Britain. The curlew sandpiper has been recorded in Nottinghamshire from 28 July to early October for main movement, and only in 1948 were birds present into November. Peak numbers tend to occur from mid-August to the end of September (max 100 in 1946), but in recent years lack of suitable feeding areas has reduced the numbers which tarry to around 5–12 birds.

Sanderling   Calidris alba (Pallas)

Scarce passage migrant.

Very occasionally in winter, 2 records, 1948 and 1963.

The spring migration may give records from the end of March

to the first week of June. Single birds are the rule, but up to 15 have been seen.

During autumn there can be a trickle through Nottinghamshire from as early as mid-July to the end of September. Latest record 29 October.

Broad-billed sandpiper   Limicola falcinellus (Pontoppidan)
Rare passage migrant.
   1 in 1961.

Ruff   Philomachus pugnax (Linnaeus)
Fairly common passage migrant. Rare winter visitor, now irregular.

During the spring passage this species may be seen from mid-March to the first week of June.

Exceptional early dates for autumn passage have been 16 and 19 June but, on average, this movement begins in early July and birds can be regularly seen during August and September, with tail-enders in October.

A few linger outside the migratory dates and can be termed wintering birds, being present during November, December and during the early months of the year if the weather is mild, but only on occasions since 1962.

Avocet   Recurvirostra avosetta Linnaeus
Rare passage migrant.
   12 records (5 reports to 1893; 7 reports 1948–72).

Appearances have been a little more frequent in recent years (thanks to Minsmere and Havergate, perhaps), and all TVBW sightings have been in the spring between 7 April and early June. Whitaker mentioned 2 birds in July.

Black-winged stilt   Himantopus himantopus (Linnaeus)
Rare vagrant. Bred 1945, the first and only breeding so far for the British Isles.
   1 record, 1946.

Grey phalarope   Phalaropus fulicarius (Linnaeus)
Rare passage migrant.
   10 records (6 reports, Whitaker to 1914; 4 reports, 1947, 1957, 1960, 1962, TVBW).
   Obviously victims of autumnal storms, these birds came from 15 September to 1 November.

Red-necked phalarope   Phalaropus lobatus (Linnaeus)
Rare passage migrant.
   4 records, 1843, 1946, 1947, 1963.
   All the dates for this dainty phalarope are also for the autumn, and fall at an earlier time than those for the grey phalarope, from 6 July (Whitaker) to 21 September.

Wilson's phalarope   Phalaropus tricolor (Vieillot)
Rare vagrant.
   1 in 1961.

Stone curlew   Burhinus oedicnemus (Linnaeus)
Rare vagrant.
   2 reports, 13 August 1953 and 13 September 1957.
   Formerly summer visitor, last successful breeding 1891 (Whitaker).

Arctic skua   Stercorarius parasiticus (Linnaeus)
Rare vagrant.
   4 records, 1 shot, undated (Whitaker); 1957, 1968, 1973 (TVBW).

Great skua   Stercorarius skua (Brünnich)
Rare vagrant.
   3 records, 1898, 1968, 1973.

Pomarine skua   Stercorarius pomarinus (Temminck)
Rare vagrant.
   1 shot, 1875 (Whitaker); 1, 1973.

Long-tailed skua   Stercorarius longicaudus Vieillot
Rare vagrant.
2 records, 1879, 1881 (Whitaker).

Great black-backed gull   Larus marinus Linnaeus
Now fairly common visitor, mainly winter.
Fairly frequent in small numbers (Whitaker); scarce visitor, any time of the year until 1960s when increase with maximum gathering 60–170, and further increase 1970s, max 700.
Although this species can be present in any month of the year, it is now coming in big numbers during the winter, and there is some evidence from roost flights etc that most of the birds have originated from the Humber area.

Lesser black-backed gull   Larus fuscus Linnaeus
Common passage migrant. Some birds, especially immatures, remain in the summer. Breeding attempted 1945, 1960 and 1961, and successful 1963 and 1964. Usually scarce at mid-winter.
With variations and fluctuations according to the weather and food available, the annual rhythm for this species begins in January when only a few birds are usually present. There is some increase during February, but definite northerly flight usually begins in early March and this return migration continues to early June. Gatherings of 40–80, occasionally 200–400 are present at various waters during this movement period. Return movement begins by the end of June and big numbers can be present during July. Sometimes a second peak can occur from September to early October, but feeding conditions and weather often cause a levelling of numbers during the long drawn-out movement to the south. Maximum roost numbers during this period can be up to 3,000 birds. Gradually, most years, numbers fall during November and, some time in December, according to the severity of the weather, the autumn movement comes to an end.

Herring gull   Larus argentatus Pontoppidan
Generally a fairly common winter visitor increasing from the late 1950s to become common. Rare in summer. Probably also a

passage migrant. Whitaker did not consider it at all common, although fairly frequent in winter and early spring.

Small numbers appear in September which build up to a peak in late autumn most years. Maximum reached 1,000 by 1970. After the worst of winter, departure can be from February, but usually the last numbers depart in March and April. A few birds appear in May (usually 1–2 birds, but maximum 40) which pass through to the north. Individuals, mostly immatures, will spend June in Nottinghamshire with the lesser black-backed gulls. In August there is an appearance and southerly movement of a few birds.

Common gull   Larrus canus Linnaeus
Uncommon winter visitor and passage migrant. Some increase by 1970 to a maximum of 500 birds associated with refuse tips. Bred successfully 1967–9, and probably bred 1970.

Movements similar to those for the herring gull. As a winter visitor a few appear in September and there can be a build-up to good numbers by late autumn. Departure is from the end of winter, from February to April according to weather. There is frequently a north-easterly movement across the county during April which, some years, may be delayed until May. Very small numbers remain during June. First return migration is noticeable at the end of July and into August, usually of a few single birds.

Glaucous gull   Larus hyperboreus Gunnerus
Rare winter visitor.

6 records, 1872, 1946, 1949, 1963, 1971, 1972. Increase in frequency during recent years thought to be due to association with the great black-backed gulls.

Iceland gull   Larus glaucoides Meyer
Rare winter visitor.

7 records, 1946, 1949, 1951, 1962, 1970, 1971, 1973. Recent increase in frequency as with the glaucous gull.

> *Glaucous/Iceland gull sp.*   Birds with the characteristics of these species were 1970 (glaucous) and 1967 and 1970 (Iceland).

Mediterranean gull   Larus melanocephalus Temminck
Rare vagrant.
    1 in 1971.

Little gull   Larus minutus Pallas
Scarce passage migrant and winter visitor, most years from 1950, increased number of sightings in recent years.
    Whitaker reported 2, 1870, 1892.
    The little gull has occurred in every month, but most records are during the spring and autumn movements, in May, and from August to September.

Black-headed gull   Larus ridibundus Linnaeus
Common resident, population very variable due to human predation, loss of habitat, industrial destruction of nest sites, etc; breeding pairs have been as low as 33 and as high as c 700. First recorded breeding, 1928.
    Passage migrant and winter visitor when 5,000–7,000 usual maximum. Arrival and departure of these wintering birds is extremely variable according to weather. Many come from the Baltic area.
    There is a random dispersal of our local stock, especially of first-year age (see p 91).

Sabine's gull   Larus sabini Sabine
Rare vagrant.
    1 in 1950.

Kittiwake   Rissa tridactyla (Linnaeus)
Rare vagrant, irregular.

Black tern   Chlidonias niger (Linnaeus)
Uncommon passage migrant. Drift rushes, however, occasionally bring over 100 birds.
    Spring migration has been observed from 12 April to 25 June and the return south from 14 July to 29 October. The birds observed in Nottinghamshire are invariably associated with easterly winds.

White-winged black tern   Chlidonias leucopterus (Temminck)
Rare passage migrant.

 5 records, 1945, 1946, 1952, 1956, 1957.

Gull-billed tern   Gelochelidon nilotica (Gmelin)
Rare vagrant.

 1 in 1945.

Caspian tern   Hydroprogne caspia (Pallas)
Rare passage migrant.

 5 records, 1863 (Whitaker); 1, undated, Colwick (Wollaton Hall Museum); 1966 (2 reports), 1970 (TVBW).

Common tern   Sterna hirundo Linnaeus
Scarce summer visitor, breeding first proved 1945. Fairly common passage migrant.

Only the common tern has settled in as an inland breeding species. During this period of at least 25 years to 1970 it has varied in numbers from 5–17 pairs, averaging c 10 pairs, and although it was first found breeding on fallow land belonging to the Nottingham Sewage Farm, the majority of nesting sites have been on islets at gravel pits. Subject to predation including egg-collectors, to disturbance from earth-moving machinery, and to flooding during excessively wet weather, the common tern's breeding has never seemed really to prosper from year to year and yet it has maintained itself. Probably the main limiting factor in the long run has been an insufficiency of correct nesting sites. Power-station fly ash has destroyed 2 good areas.

The earliest spring date is 2 April and there are 6 records (TVBW) of early birds for the period 11–18 April. Usual first arrivals are during the fourth week of April. Passage can begin in late April, normally during May and June. Some years numbers are rather spectacular as parties of up to 40 go through. First birds moving south are seen during July with main passage in August and into September. Last stragglers are during October, with 14 November latest date.

Arctic tern   Sterna paradisaea Pontoppidan
Scarce passage migrant.

This species is under-recorded because of difficulties of positive identification when in flight. Spring arrival is a little later than that for the common tern with the first birds appearing during the first week of May. General movement during May and June is often in association with the common tern. Migration south is similar, however, with the first birds around mid-July, and general passage from then until September with stragglers into October. Of positively identified birds, 8 October is the latest date for Nottinghamshire.

Roseate tern   Sterna dougallii Montagu
Rare passage migrant.

4 records, 1945, 1966, 1970 (2).

Little tern   Sterna albifrons Pallas
Scarce passage migrant, most years.

Northward passage in the spring has been recorded between the inclusive dates of 1 May and 29 June, with the main movement between mid-May and mid-June. Return migration has begun as early as 5 July and birds have been seen from then on, with August and September the peak period, and 5 October the last date.

Sandwich tern   Sterna sandvicensis Latham
Scarce passage migrant, most years.

Early birds have appeared in March on 3 occasions (20 March the earliest) and movement has been recorded during April, May and to the end of June. 5 July is the earliest date for movement to the south, and the peak period during August and September agrees with the other tern species. Of the two October dates for the sandwich tern, 21 October is the latest.

Razorbill   Alca torda Linnaeus
Rare vagrant.

2 records, 1847, 1870 (Whitaker).

Little auk   Alle alle (Linnaeus)
Storm-driven vagrant.

16 records (7 reports 1841–1906; 10 reports, 1911–71, which includes 1 collective report of 17 birds in Nottinghamshire connected with the wreck of 1912.

Birds have occurred from November to February and most have been found during November and January.

Guillemot   Uria aalge (Pontoppidan)
Rare vagrant.

1 in 1855 (Sterland).

Puffin   Fratercula arctica (Linnaeus)
Rare vagrant.

4 records, 1884, 1917, 1944, 1953.

Pallas's sandgrouse   Syrrhaptes paradoxus (Pallas)
Rare vagrant.

12–14 birds, 1863; over 60 birds, possibly 100+, 1888 (Whitaker); adult male, shot 24 May 1888, Costock; present, Besthorpe, no date (Oates).

Stock dove   Columba oenas Linnaeus
Fairly common resident. Reduced numbers from 1960s (TVBW).

Whitaker considered that the stock dove increased between 1886 and 1906 to become plentiful in the forest areas, where there were many nest sites in the old trees. Perhaps because of few nest sites this species was less numerous in the north and south of Nottinghamshire.

During the period 1945–59 it was considered as a widespread breeding bird and common in many areas. By 1960, however, it was listed as fairly common and it took the effects of the severe 1962–3 winter to bring home the fact that this species had declined. For the 1960s its status was uncommon, with a little improvement in numbers towards the end of the decade. Hedgerow clearance must have robbed this bird of many nest sites in the less well-wooded parts of the county.

Woodpigeon   Columba palumbus Linnaeus
Common resident. Abundant at times, especially winter.

Forever persecuted, the woodpigeon has endured many hazards, including recent heavy losses during the toxic seed-dressing years of 1959–61 and then the killing 1962–3 winter, yet it remains a common breeding species. Long may it do so, because it is an attractive inhabitant of our farmlands, and from a sporting and an amenity point of view its value must largely offset the damage it does. No one seems to mention how this so-called pest spends a considerable amount of time feeding on the seeds of wild plants, even when the corn is ripe!

Density on farmland is difficult to assess, owing to nest destruction and predation, but up to 10 pairs per 100 acres would be approximately average. In woodland the density is greater, from 10–20 pairs per 100 acres, and possibly more where conifer plantations border farmland.

Movements have been recorded by local birdwatchers studying visual passerine arrival in the autumn and hard-weather movements. Woodpigeons come to Nottinghamshire from the north-east or east and can be English birds born in Lincolnshire or perhaps in other eastern counties, but the possibility of some Continental stock cannot be ruled out.

Turtle dove   Streptopelia turtur (Linnaeus)
Fairly common summer visitor and passage migrant.

Whitaker gave 1868 as the first authenticated breeding for this species, although 1 or 2 birds were present in Nottinghamshire just prior to this (rare, 1866, Felkin). From this period he reported that this new colonist 'increased year by year till now [1906] we find them well dispersed over the county'.

The turtle dove found a suitable niche among our farmland community and, as its food comprised mainly the seeds of common weeds such as fumitory, plantain, persicaria and chickweed, it continued to prosper up to present times. Classified as fairly common, no alteration in its status has been detected in spite of modern farming techniques including weed spraying and monoculture which, it is felt, must have affected its food supply in some localities.

The small sample of farms surveyed reveals that, at about 1 pair per 100 acres, this dove does not rank as a dominant farm species. It will use all types of woodland edges for nesting and, possibly, density is a little higher in areas of farmland carrying plenty of woodland.

Whitaker recorded his first birds for 35 years from 1872 to 1906 and his dates for one observer reveal quite adequately the pattern of arrival for this species. He had 1 early year, 16 April 1893, while the other 7 April dates were 28th–30th. His firsts for another 9 of the years were 1–4 May. 12 of his records were for 6–11 May, and the last 6 tailed off to 26 May, representing the late years.

TVBW records by many observers from 1942–70 widen the range a little, but do not alter Whitaker's pattern. Occasionally an individual of this species comes through way ahead of its fellows, eg 2 April (the earliest for Notts) in 1970 and 5 April in 1966. The usual first birds are from 16 April, most of these early ones arriving during the fourth week of April, and general arrival begins in early May.

Departure is from August, with the last birds during the second half of September (21–23 September occurs fairly regularly), and late stragglers have been recorded 6 times in October with the 14th the latest date.

Collared dove   Streptopelia decaocto (Frivaldszky)
Generally a common resident.

This species colonised England in the 1950s much as the turtle dove did long ago. The first proved breeding in Nottinghamshire was at Osberton in 1959, although it was suspected that breeding may have been attempted in 1958. The words of Whitaker can be used again, because the collared dove similar to the turtle dove 'has increased year by year and is well dispersed over the county'.

Unlike the turtle dove, this species readily uses man as a food provider, much as the house sparrow does, and its niche includes corn mills, poultry farms, pig farms, parks and garden bird tables.

The probable colonisation of Nottinghamshire can be seen in two clear phases: 1, the first birds, and subsequently, the first colonies were set up near corn mills in the Worksop area c 1959 and in the Newark area in 1961. From these country towns birds spread outwards until many square miles were occupied, and there was a return to the corn mills during the winter.

It is probable that a similar start and spread originated at the corn mills of Gainsborough which helped in the colonisation of North Nottinghamshire, but this area is not well covered by ornithologists. By 1963 the Nottingham area was taken over, public feeding in the parks such as the Arboretum and in the gardens enabling the birds to settle. Phase 2, perhaps helped by further immigration, saw the gradual appearance of this 'gentle invader' at most of our villages, and this process of in-filling was well advanced by 1968 when a winter flock of 300 was reported for Worksop.

Status at 1970 stands at 'common for many areas, but uncommon/fairly common in some places'.

Conifers are favoured for nests, although deciduous trees will be used. As yet this species seems to be much less reliant on true woodland.

Cuckoo   Cuculus canorus Linnaeus
Common summer visitor.

The survey areas each held a pair or had a bird present, and it could well be that this species requires more than 200 acres of farmland for a female and its mate. Probably the dunnock is the main foster species in this habitat.

Because it is seen so often flying over the fields about its business, this species is not generally looked upon as a woodland bird. However, it is a member of this community, especially in the heathland and the more open areas, and its density here is only slightly greater than it is on the farmland. P. M. Hope once found 6 nests (5 blackcaps and 1 garden warbler) with cuckoo eggs in 1 acre of Stage 1 conifer woodland.

The cuckoo can utilise both the farmland and the woodland at the same time.

Whitaker commented, after reviewing his arrival list from 1871 to 1906, that it was 'strong evidence against March arrivals, heard or seen, never obtained'. His earliest bird was on 10 April and for the years reviewed the general time of arrival was from 20 April. TVBW have one record for a March cuckoo, in 1962. It was seen closely in Holme Pierrepont village by two observers as it hawked insects on 25 and 26 March and, 3 days later, was heard and then seen 3 miles away at Burton Joyce. The next earliest date is 5 April. From 1942–70 the arrival of the cuckoo can be summarised as follows: very early birds usually arrive 9–12 April, normal vanguard individuals appear from mid-April and general arrival, as shown by Whitaker, takes place during the fourth week of April. Cold springs delay some arrival into May.

Movement south probably begins in July, but it is difficult to prove, and records show definite movement during August and into September to the 23rd. Occasionally, birds are seen into October and there is a record of one for 18 November.

Barn owl   Tyto alba (Scopoli)
Fairly common resident.

Truly this species is the farmland owl. Whitaker reported it as thinly diffused over the county, but more plentiful in the forest country for the period 1850–1906. He remarked that it was wonderful how little they were seen even where they were plentiful. Since then the motor car has caused numbers to be seen as corpses at the roadside.

TVBW records agree with the above, showing that it is fairly common bearing in mind its territorial requirements. It is to be found throughout the county and, roughly, a pair are established every 2 miles. The greatest density according to reports was for the Forest and Dukeries area, where at least 10 pairs were present on c 1,400 acres. Dr A. D. Scott, following many years of study, considered there were 14–20 pairs of barn owls to 200 square kilometres, ie around 2 pairs per square mile, in part of north Nottinghamshire with a farmland habitat.

From the above and taking the county as a whole, poor barn owl areas as well as good, a density of 1–2 pairs per square mile would be average.

Scops owl   Otus scops (Linnaeus)
Rare vagrant. 1, 1973.

Little owl   Athene noctua (Scopoli)
Fairly common resident.

This owl, introduced to England from 1874, was found in Nottinghamshire in 1896 (Whitaker). More were seen 1901–4, from when it became well established.

During the 1940s it was considered common, especially in the rough pasture land of the Trent Valley. It was frequently seen during daylight hours.

During post-war years (1950–70) it became more nocturnal and somewhat less common, although of wide and general distribution. As a farmland species it is associated with hedgerow trees for nesting and with mixed farmland.

Dr A. D. Scott considered that about 3 pairs to the square mile were present in north Nottinghamshire.

Tawny owl   Strix aluco Linnaeus
Common resident.

Considered to be rarer than the barn owl by both Sterland and Whitaker, TVBW records show it to be the commoner, perhaps because it is not confined to one main habitat. It is difficult to name an area of Nottinghamshire where it is not present at some time in the year, even including town and city. Dr A. D. Scott for his 10 square miles considered there were up to 40 pairs present (4 pairs to the square mile) which is double the number for the barn owl, and TVBW findings for Nottinghamshire as a whole support this density.

Long-eared owl   Asio otus (Linnaeus)
Scarce resident, local. Some winter visitors.

Whitaker may have been confused about the status of the

tawny owl and this species because, although he states that the tawny is the rarer, he also remarks that the long-eared owl is not common.

TVBW findings have always found it to be local and mainly confined to the areas of permanent grassland (but rare in Trent Valley) and to the Forest country. At one time this species would have been classed as nearly rare, but the new forestry seems to be influencing an increase. Dr A. D. Scott considers there are 30–50 breeding pairs in the whole of Nottinghamshire, and TVBW records support the minimal figure of around 30 pairs.

Short-eared owl   Asio flammeus (Pontoppidan)
Scarce winter visitor and passage migrant.

Good years 1884 and several subsequent years; 20 shot, 1872, and 8 in one other area.

Bred 1908; summer records at times; eggs predated, 1973.

The early birds arrive in August (earliest 1 August) and in September. General arrival from October, and often remains in Nottinghamshire until the end of April. Records show late stragglers to end of May.

Nighthawk   Chordeiles minor (Forster)
Rare vagrant.

1 in 1971.

Nightjar   Caprimulgus europaeus Linnaeus
Uncommon summer visitor, local.

In the times of Sterland and Whitaker this bird was quite familiar to them on the sandy lands of Rainworth and Edwinstowe, where they considered it to be fairly plentiful. It is safe to state that this must have been its status from Bestwood near Nottingham to the Yorkshire border along the sandstone. Elsewhere, apart from the border sands with Lincolnshire, it was not well known and Whitaker stated that it was rare. Did the nightjar really breed away from the sandy areas?

Its numbers decreased during the first 30 years of the 20th

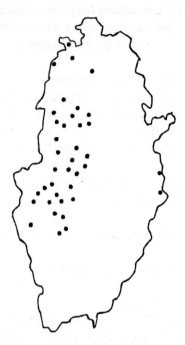

NIGHTJAR 1942-70
● Recorded breeding

century, and locally the cause seemed to be connected with loss of breeding habitat and, possibly, with human pressure causing disturbance. During the last 30 or so years it has held its own and, with the coming of active forestry, may have increased a little. It is confined to areas of heathland and to open woodland on our sandy soils, where certain places here and there hold several pairs in loose colonies. Assessment of the numbers is difficult for this crespuscular species and TVBW records can only show a minimal estimate which is approximately 60 pairs.

The earliest date on record is 21 April (Sterland, 1847). Whitaker's first dates for the years 1873 to 1906 were from 24 April to 8 June for the 26 years when records were made. An analysis showed 2 April dates (24th and 28th) and the rest were spread fairly evenly throughout May; he considered the two June dates late on his part and not on the birds'. His records suggest that 10–16 May (8 years out of the 26) may be general for Rainworth.

It is not always easy to obtain first-arrival dates for this species. TVBW findings are that it does appear at the end of April, but such earliness is rare. First arrivals are during the first half of May with the period 10–16 May (as suggested by Whitaker's dates) for the general arrival time, with further arrivals to the end of the month.

Birds out of habitat are few and, of those recorded, the departure period is from 8 August to 20 September.

Egyptian nightjar   Caprimulgus aegyptius (Lichtenstein)
Rare vagrant.

1 in 1883. The only record for Britain.

Swift   Apus apus (Linnaeus)
Common summer visitor and passage migrant.

The earliest for this species is 4 April (Sterland). Nearly 20% of Whitaker's first sightings were in April and main arrival was 3–10 May.

TVBW records were from more observers and also included the Trent Valley, where aerial feeders often congregate in the spring. 80% of these records (1942–70) were of first arrivals in April. The years 1958, 1960, 1962 and 1968 were marked by good numbers arriving during April. However, the general trend is that small numbers arrive during the second half of April, while good numbers and main arrival are usually in the first week of May or before the 15th. Cold springs and movement of birds to the north of Nottinghamshire cause gatherings at feeding areas during the second half of May.

Migration southwards begins in July, with good numbers at times in the first week, possibly of non-breeding birds. Usually the movement gains momentum during the second half of July and there is a brisk exodus into the first 10 or so days of August. By

164

the middle of August few Nottinghamshire birds are left and this remnant soon departs. The last few linger into September, and last dates reach the fourth week. Some years this timing is a little later and the whole of the main departure can be throughout August and, conversely, local birds sometimes leave very promptly and there are no swifts for days until a sudden flurry occurs. These later birds are considered to be passage birds from elsewhere associated with falls of migrants on the east coast. TVBW records have 5 dates for October birds and 1 very late report of 2 birds on 12 November.

Kingfisher   Alcedo atthis (Linnaeus)
Uncommon resident.

The map of Notts rivers and streams with the level of pollution indicated (page 56) is sufficient to demonstrate the breeding areas of the kingfisher. Wherever there are sufficient small fish this colourful little bird will be found. Up to the late 1930s it was present on every stretch of unpolluted water but, since the war, its extent of breeding range has to be qualified. Now, at the beginning of the 1970s, it is present on those waters which provide a bank for nesting as well as the fish.

It can be seen beside the River Trent and, except where there are trees overhanging suitable shallows, such riverside birds are usually hurrying from one inflowing stream to the next, preferring these to the wide, deep river.

The kingfisher was almost wiped out during the severe 1962–3 winter and a return to something approaching normal numbers took at least 5 years.

Bee-eater   Merops apiaster Linnaeus
Rare vagrant.

2 records, 1878, 1970.

Roller   Coracias garrulus Linnaeus
Rare vagrant.

1, 1966, which may have been an escaped bird.

Hoopoe   Upupa epops Linnaeus
Rare vagrant.

At least 13 records (6 or more, 1863–1910, Whitaker; 7 reports, 1934–72, TVBW).

Green woodpecker   Picus viridis Linnaeus
Fairly common resident to early 1960s. Uncommon resident, 1963–73.

Both Sterland and Whitaker referred to this woodpecker as a woodland species. From 1935 to about 1960 the TVBW knew it as fairly common, with numbers nesting in hedgerow trees away from woods in association with permanent pasture. Following the 1962–3 hard winter when this species was considerably reduced, recovery was not good. The ploughing up of old grassland and the continual disturbance of the big ant-hills affected the green woodpecker adversely.

Of the 3 species both Sterland and Whitaker considered this the commonest. Whitaker mentioned that 'although it looks a strong bird many perish in severe frosts'.

Since 1963 the Birklands and Dukeries areas held most of the few survivors and now, in 1970, it has spread considerably, but there are still many woodlands where its laughing call is a sound of the past.

Even at its most numerous it was always a minor member of the woodland community at about 2 pairs per 100 acres.

Great spotted woodpecker   Dendrocopus major (Linnaeus)
Fairly common resident.

Generally this species has been more common and widespread than the green woodpecker during the last 30 years, the opposite to what Sterland and Whitaker found. Density would probably average out at a pair to 50 acres of hardwoods, but less in mainly conifer areas.

Immigrants from the Continent arrive during the autumn and presumably winter with us before returning in the spring.

Lesser spotted woodpecker   Dendrocopus minor (Linnaeus)
Scarce resident, Local.

Always scarce, this small woodpecker appears to have a patchy distribution (see map below), and the centre of the Forest country is its main stronghold.

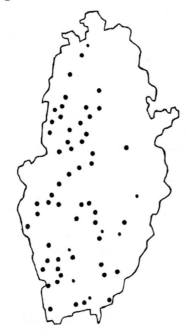

LESSER SPOTTED WOODPECKER
1942 - 70

● Recorded breeding
· Birds present

Wryneck   Jynx torquilla Linnaeus
Rare passage migrant, occasional.

Formerly rare summer visitor. Breeding suspected 1944, 1954, 1955.

This elusive species can be overlooked very easily. Spring migrants are extremely rare and TVBW have only 3 dates, 16 and 23 April and 21 May. Birds moving through during the autumn are more frequent and occur when good falls of wrynecks have taken place on the east coast. There is one August date, the 27th, but most are recorded during September; latest date 25 October.

Short-toed lark   Calandrella cinerea (Gmelin)
Rare vagrant.
   1 in 1950.

Woodlark   Lullula arborea (Linnaeus)
Formerly uncommon resident, local.
   Rare, and probably not breeding from 1969.
   The mellow, liquid notes of this accomplished songster were a feature of the heathy grassland areas dotted about the woodlands on the sandy soils. Whitaker never saw it and Sterland, living close to one of its main areas, considered it rare. In the 1950s it was present in some 30 areas, but appeared gradually to decline after 1960, so that it may now, in 1970, be a lost breeding bird. Loss of habitat, and the disappearance of the rabbit with myxomatosis plus the severe 1962–3 winter, must have contributed to the decline, but also, Nottinghamshire being at the extreme northern edge of its range, a temporary retreat may be taking place.

Skylark   Alauda arvensis Linnaeus
Common resident, passage migrant and winter visitor.
   Considered abundant by Sterland and one of the commonest of Nottinghamshire's birds by Whitaker, it is pleasing that this cheerful songster is still very much with us in spite of modern farming. Density in the 1960s was from 8–16 pairs per 100 acres.
   There is a little evidence of a few arrivals from late July and during August, but the main period of movement by the Continental birds begins in September, usually from the second week, and this migration (SW, W, or NW) continues right into November, to the last few days in some years. If persistent westerly winds check this arrival there can be quite spectacular visual movement when the weather becomes favourable. October is, on average, the month of peak numbers.

Further movement from the eastern side of Britain and from our county takes place at the onset of hard weather, especially with snow.

Return easterly movement at winter's end is less well recorded. The period late February to early April emerges from TVBW records, with March the main departure month.

Shore lark   Eremophila alpestris (Linnaeus)
Rare vagrant.
    2 records, 1945, 1973.

Swallow   Hirundo rustica Linnaeus
Common summer visitor and passage migrant.

Of the hirundines, it is safe to report that the swallow is very much the farmland species, and the majority of our birds breed in farm buildings or in buildings close to the fields. If farmers could (and would) fill in an inquiry about swallows, the total number in Nottinghamshire would be surprisingly large.

Whitaker did not record any swallows in March and, of his first arrivals, 64% arrived in the period 12–16 April.

Favourable weather in March will influence an early arrival of a single bird or a few individuals and TVBW records show that first dates for swallows were obtained 7 times for March from 1942–70, which is 25% of the years involved. The earliest bird came on 26 March. The general pattern of arrival, however, is for the first bird and the early few to appear during the first week of April. Occasionally, there is good arrival during the second week but, more often, cold winds can almost halt the build-up right into the third week. Towards the end of this week more birds are seen, especially in the Trent Valley and often, in April's fourth week, large numbers reach Nottinghamshire.

Southern relates the swallow's arrival to the movement north of the 48° F (9° C) isotherm.

Further arrival and through migration continues until about 10 May under normal conditions, but this passage migration can be delayed till late May in some years.

First departures have been noticed in July, usually in the second fortnight, and these presage the building up of numbers moving southward during August. Large flocks rarely occur before the middle of August and, without doubt, the peak time for this species in Nottinghamshire, when visual movement is brisk and when large numbers congregate in night roosts, is from late August into September, until about the 25th. Flight direction can vary between south-east, south and south-west.

There is no shortage of swallows in early October; they generally consist of many family parties which, because they are present in every village area, give the impression of large numbers. However, they are the rearguard, and daily recording often ends by the third week. From then on few birds remain and, although November birds are almost annual, in the main they concern only the last individuals. The latest date recorded is 24 November.

House martin   *Delichon urbica (Linnaeus)*
Fairly common/common summer visitor and passage migrant.

Although included as a farmland species because of groups and colonies based on farms, the house martin is really a village and suburban bird.

It is widespread about our country homes, being almost as familiar as the swallow, and in recent years, has colonised the new suburban estates successfully. It has been shown to prefer (but not 100%) those houses with an overhang which has been painted white or a similar pale shade.

The earliest and exceptional arrival date is 30 March. Really early arrivals normally appear during the first week of April, whereas, the general period for first birds is from 8 to 20 April. Some springs, being milder, have good numbers appearing from the middle of April, but the usual main arrival period is during the fourth week, an inflow checked by English springs of Arctic temperament until May (Whitaker and TVBW).

There may be some July departure from Nottinghamshire, but it is so small that it has escaped positive detection. TVBW findings show slight movement during the first half of August with no increase until the end of the month when, on a few occasions, good numbers have left. September is the main month for leaving Nottinghamshire and, according to the weather, the peak can be any time in the month. Young are regularly in the nest as late as early October, and these birds are probably part of the later October passage. In some years main departure can be during early October and southward flying flocks can be seen during those spells of ideal, sunny, Goose Fair weather. Normally, a rapid decrease in numbers takes place during October and this species becomes extremely scarce during the fourth week. Late birds in November occur fairly frequently and the last date is 23 November.

Sand martin *Riparia riparia (Linnaeus)*
Fairly common/common summer visitor and passage migrant.

This hirundine occurs in a number of widely differing habitats in our county ranging from the urban/suburban sites through railway embankments to forestland quarries, and then to the typical ones of the waterside. Even when the essential requirement of a bank for a nest hole is away from water, the birds will visit and use any nearby water for a feeding area.

The banks of the River Trent have always been used and still are, although in recent times the policy of smoothing out awkward corners to increase water-flow has reduced sites. It is perhaps as well, because the rapid rise of the Trent after big storms has flooded out vulnerable nests year after year. Gravel-pit areas have more than offset the loss of the Trentside colonies and may have contributed to a local increase.

Many years of study of the sand martin have been carried out by John McMeeking and Edward Cowley. Unfortunately, the considerable data has yet to be analysed. They did discover that some 1,400 pairs at least were breeding in Nottinghamshire around 1968, but this was followed by a huge decrease.

Living in the central part of Nottinghamshire, Whitaker saw the sand martin in March on only two occasions. His arrival dates show, however, that 60% of his first birds came before 14 April.

TVBW records, covering the Trent Valley, which is favoured by early hirundines, reveal that March arrival took place for 77% of the years from 1942–70. The sand martin precedes the swallow both in first birds and in the arrival of numbers, and in warm March weather, such as prevailed in 1957, really good numbers will arrive.

The first sand martin was seen in 7 years out of the 64 during the period 12–19 March (TVBW records of 5 out of 26 is more realistic) and the period 22–31 March stands out as the general first arrival time. 1–5 April represents delayed first arrivals due to cold weather. Occasionally this species is caught by really severe weather, when lethargy sets in and some birds die. Also, reverse migration has been suspected. During unusually backward springs the main arrival is checked and then coincides with that for the swallow and house martin.

Through migration often continues until well into May.

The sand martin, perhaps because it is easily observed, has revealed east-west movement during the spring more than any other species. The first S–SW movement begins as early as the beginning of July (2 July in 1967) and this exodus often becomes obvious during the second half of the month when flocks of up to 600 can be recorded. August is the main month for departure with occasional big numbers during the first 2 weeks of September. Often there is an abrupt end to this exodus, with the last birds around 25–26 September. October is the month of the few dawdlers, usually till about the middle of the month. There are 3 late dates—12 and 28 November, and 1 December.

Golden oriole   Oriolus oriolus (Linnaeus)
Rare passage migrant.

7 records (1863, 1889, 1913, 1917, Whitaker; 1947, 1957, 1964, TVBW).

Raven   Corvus corax Linnaeus
Rare vagrant.

At least 13 records (6 or more reports, Whitaker; 7 reports, 1920–72).

Carrion crow   Corvus corone (Linnaeus)
Common resident.

Sterland described it as rarely seen in greater numbers than a single pair and Whitaker considered it a scarce to rare species which, sometimes, was not seen by him for a number of years.

Man's hand is still against this predacious crow which, with the decline of the game preserve, is now quite common. Winter roosts of up to 220 (Gunthorpe, 1962) have been reported. Most of these belong to the 'wild' places such as gravel-pit areas, rough scrubland etc, and although widespread on farmland it is of thin distribution.

Hooded crow   Corvus corone cornix Linnaeus
Uncommon winter visitor 1940s, now rare.

Formerly regular winter visitor, 72 at a roost, 1887, Whitaker.

Rook   Corvus frugilegus Linnaeus
Common resident.

Always a common bird, censuses have shown fluctuations in the numbers breeding in Nottinghamshire. Records (in nests):

1928	6,576	7·7 per square mile	(A. Roebuck)
1932	6,113	7·2 per square mile	(A. Roebuck)
1944	10,163	12·2 per square mile	(A. I. H. Docksey & A. Roebuck)
1958	17,028	20 per square mile	(TVBW)
1962	10,609	12·5 per square mile	(TVBW)

The large increase found by the TVBW count in 1958 was attributed to more land being under corn. The repeat 1962 count revealed that nests were almost back to the 1944 level. This count followed the years 1959–61 when poisonous seed-dressings of the chlorinated hydrocarbon group (Aldrin, Dieldrin etc) were used extensively. Bird-watchers and landowners found dead rooks lying about the fields or beneath rookeries.

No county census has been carried out since 1962, but sample counts and occasional area counts have revealed very little increase since then and, possibly, the rook is now at a density of approximately 13 nests per square mile. The distribution of the rook is not even, however (see map, page 30), and the greatest concentration is in the eastern half of the county on the damper, heavier land of the Keuper Marl and Lower Lias, and on the alluvium of the Trent Valley. There are approximately 2 pairs of rooks per 100 acres for the county as a whole, and possibly up to 4 pairs per 100 acres in the areas of densest population.

Jackdaw   Corvus monedula Linnaeus
Common resident.

A field species which uses woodland for nesting purposes and is most numerous in areas where nest-holes in old hardwoods are available. For this reason alone it is a member of the woodland community and a pair can be expected in any small wood if there is a suitable nesting site. The competition among jackdaws, owls, kestrels and stockdoves for the nest-holes must be fierce, especially in farmland areas where the hedgerow trees have been reduced.

The Dukeries hold several thousands at times, far outnumbering the rooks there. However, in the farmland areas the ratio is more even.

Magpie   Pica pica (Linnaeus)
Common resident.

This species is more of an open farmland species than the jackdaw and, before the great conversion to arable began, it was a familiar enough bird in the grassland areas such as the Vale of Belvoir and the Wolds. Distribution seems to be 1–2 pairs per 100 acres in many areas, although it can be scarce in others.

It has become regular in urban and suburban areas during the last thirty years.

Nutcracker   Nucifraga caryocatactes (Linnaeus)
Rare vagrant.

2 records, 1871, 1883.

Jay   Garrulus glandarius (Linnaeus)
Fairly common resident.

This woodland crow becomes conspicuous during the autumn when it works for several weeks collecting and burying the acorn crop. Otherwise it is inconspicuous, and especially so during the breeding season.

Well distributed in the forest in both hardwood and softwood, it is also a member of the birdlife in the larger woods throughout the county. Fortunately for the smaller nesting birds it is not too numerous, and must be in the region of 2 pairs to 100 acres with a higher concentration in parts of the forest country.

Great tit   Parus major Linnaeus
Common resident.

This species is a successful member of the deciduous woodland and there must be up to 20 pairs per 100 acres with a much smaller density in less hospitable habitats. In the outer suburbs it is probably at 2–3 pairs per 100 acres.

Blue tit   Parus caeruleus Linnaeus
Common resident.

This species, able to scrape a living with only a few trees, is more numerous than the great tit and in the best deciduous woodland it must average out at 30–40 pairs per 100 acres. Conifer populations are low and are controlled by the lack or presence of deciduous trees and availability of nest sites. In suburbia it is around three times more numerous than the great tit and at 6–10 pairs per 100 acres.

Coal tit   Parus ater Linnaeus
Fairly common resident; common in coniferous woodland areas.

Although widespread the coal tit is not numerous in the farmland deciduous woods and can be absent altogether during the breeding season. More are present in mixed woodland, and the increase in conifers has, without a doubt, created a greater breeding area for it locally. It is often the only bird to break the silence of the Forestry Commission forest where, it is felt, numbers are not complete because of a scarcity of nest sites, although bracken roots and bunched fronds may offer many cavities. From 1 pair to 100 acres in deciduous woods it is probably as numerous as 6–8 pairs per 100 acres in mature or overmature soft or evenly mixed woods.

> *Great tit, blue tit and coal tit* Irruptions and arrival of Continental birds takes place at times and, also, our British stock is subject to movement.

Marsh tit   Parus palustris Linnaeus
Fairly common resident.

This brown bird with the black cap can be found throughout the county and is the usual tit to be found in our deciduous woodland, alongside both great tit and blue tit, being more common than the coal tit at a density of around 6 pairs to the 100 acres. Broken down to fit the usual small woods it represents at least a pair in a 10-acre wood.

In the forest country it overlaps with the willow tit, but this does not appear to affect its numbers.

Willow tit   Parus montanus von Baldenstein
Uncommon/fairly common resident, rather local distribution.

Neither Sterland nor Whitaker knew this species, which is so difficult to differentiate from the marsh tit, and all their willow tits were marsh! Such simplicity could not be used by the TVBW and, painstakingly, a knowledge of its distribution is being built up, though still incomplete.

The willow tit is not as numerous nor as evenly spread as the marsh tit. This may be partly due to habitat preference, for whereas the marsh tit is equally at home in wet or dry situations, the willow tit prefers damp woodlands. *The Handbook of British Birds* states that this preference, although not exclusive, may derive from the greater opportunity for finding nesting sites in rotted stumps of birch, alder and elder. Significantly, where the willow tit is most numerous in Nottinghamshire, there is plenty of suitable habitat in damp woodland consisting of the above-named trees.

In the forest country, from Beauvale, Felley, Annesley, New-stead and Oxton Bogs in the south, to the Yorkshire border in the north, the willow tits are at their highest density and can be

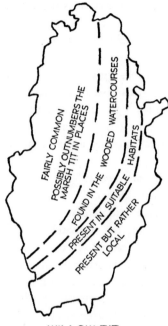

WILLOW TIT
Breeding season distribution

termed locally fairly common. This main breeding area gets a mention in the *Handbook* as follows: 'In northern Notts., and in part of S. Yorks., has been found to be the commoner, and in some areas the only black-capped tit.'

Density is probably around 6–8 pairs per 100 acres. Elsewhere the willow tit is local or rare, and our knowledge is detailed on the distribution map for this species (see above).

Long-tailed tit   Aegithalos caudatus (Linnaeus)
Fairly common resident.

A familiar enough species to birdwatchers and yet one which does not show up well in statistics. Numerically it can be placed on a par with the marsh tit, being found throughout the county and probably averaging around 6 pairs to 100 acres of suitable habitat in well-wooded country. It is quite at home in conifers.

Bearded tit   Panurus biarmicus (Linnaeus)
Rare winter visitor.

5 records, c 1850, 1908, 1965–6, 1968, 1972.

The appearance of this species in Nottinghamshire in recent years is due to irruptions from the colonies of the East Anglian nature reserves and, possibly, from the increased numbers in Holland after conversion of sea areas to land.

Nuthatch   Sitta europaea Linnaeus
Fairly common resident, local.

Formerly much more widely distributed.

An oak-forest species, the nuthatch is of limited distribution (see map, page 179) and seems to be confined to areas of mature or over-mature hardwoods. Its stronghold is the Birklands and the Dukeries, and it is unlikely to spread much while softwood exceeds hardwood planting. Amenity hardwood planting could assist. No large numbers are seen anywhere, but in places such as Welbeck and Clumber density could be as high as 6 pairs per 100 acres.

Treecreeper   Certhia familiaris Linnaeus
Fairly common resident.

Another species with which everyone is familiar, observed wherever there are woods large or small, and yet it is a bit of a statistical mystery. Obviously it is overlooked but, even so, it only holds a minor position in the woodland community at probably 2–3 pairs per 100 acres. Increased conifer acreage, one would expect, ought to cause some increase.

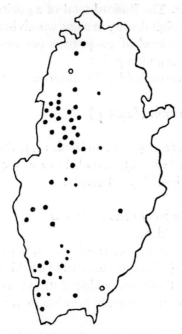

NUTHATCH 1942-70
- ● Regular breeding
- ○ Known to have bred
- • Isolated record

Density is suggested by grouping

Wren *Troglodytes troglodytes* (*Linnaeus*)
Common resident.

This ubiquitous little bird is found on our farmland mainly as a woodland species inhabiting the orchard, the farm garden and copse. It can be found living in the field hedgerow but, as any former bird-nester knows, the wren is not a true species of farm fields and their dividing hedges.

It is close to the robin as the most numerous woodland species, and its contribution to the chorus of this habitat is considerable. Its powerful song was sadly missed during the breeding season of 1963 when over 90% of the wren population had been wiped out

179

during the winter. The Rufford total of 29 pairs in 50 acres for 1968 indicates its high density in some woods but, averaging out, it is probably at a level of 30–40 pairs per 100 acres when the population is at saturation point.

The outer suburban habitat has been successfully colonised.

Dipper   *Cinclus cinclus* (*Linnaeus*)
Rare visitor.

9 or 10 records (2 or 3 shot, undated, 1873, 1881, 1898, 1890–1, 1965, 1970, 1972 (2 birds). Included is 1 example of the Continental form, the black-bellied dipper.

Mistle thrush   *Turdus viscivorus Linnaeus*
Fairly common resident.

The stormcock or sycock, as it is sometimes called in Nottinghamshire, is a bird of our pastures using a field tree or an orchard fork for its nest. Thinly but widely distributed over farmland. It does not occupy an important position in the woodland community.

For comparison with the song thrush, its density is around 2–3 pairs per 100 acres. The spacious outer suburbs of city and town have been colonised at a density of 1–2 pairs per 100 acres.

Fieldfare   *Turdus pilaris Linnaeus*
Winter visitor and passage migrant.

The earliest autumn fieldfare was seen in August (1910) and, since 1942, birds have been recorded for 10 of the Septembers, usually during the last 9 days of the month. Whitaker saw this species twice in September during his long life of birdwatching. As with all migrants the weather plays an important role in its journeys but, nevertheless, the arrival and departure times are remarkably consistent. The first birds reach Nottinghamshire during the first week of October, and later, the middle days are regularly the time for the first numbers to appear. Similarly, the latter half of October sees the really big flocks arrive and, often, this arrival and W–SW passage continues into early November.

During those Octobers when the Atlantic depressions roll end-lessly across Britain the fieldfare is held up until the winds fall favourably, when the sudden appearance of thousands on our pastures or at the hawthorn berries is really spectacular. Arrival has continued till late in November under these conditions. Hard-weather movements will result in this species becoming rare during the winter.

Departure at the end of the winter can have two features: 1, an appearance of flocks and a quick disappearance during March and into April; or 2, a steady build-up (of birds from Ireland and Western Britain perhaps?) because of stiff cold easterly winds until the county is full of restless flocks impatiently waiting for a change of wind—and then, suddenly, nearly all are gone. It is significant that 26–27 April, often a general arrival time for the summer species, is also the time when the last parties of fieldfares are seen.

Except for the occasional really late spring, stragglers into May are exceptional (only in 9 of the TVBW 28 recording years), and truly laggard birds into June have been recorded only twice— 2 June (TVBW) and 9 June (Sterland).

Song thrush   Turdus philomelos Brehm
Common resident, some emigrate. Also passage migrant.

The song thrush is quite at home on farmland preferring the mixed farm and the grassland to the arable. It was found to be more numerous on the moist lowland farms of Greenhedge Farm and Malkin Hill than on the other 2 study areas and seemed to have a density of from 4 to 8 pairs per 100 acres.

Unlike its larger relative, this species can and does occupy a niche in the woodland habitat and its density is from 12–16 pairs per 100 acres. In Grade 1–2 suburban habitat it is at around 5 pairs per 100 acres.

It is often difficult to identify migrant song thrushes especially the British birds which have moved south from northern areas. It is certain that Continental birds are part of the great movements of Turdidae from and back to Europe. The appearance of parties of wild song thrushes at the times of the redwings and fieldfares is a feature of migration-watching in Nottinghamshire from September to early November.

Redwing Turdus iliacus Linnaeus
Winter visitor and passage migrant.

The earliest autumn date for this species is 6 September. Arrival corresponds very closely to the fieldfare's except that numbers are generally smaller and through passage quicker. September arrival, 1942–70, was recorded for 11 of the years. Early numbers appear during the first week of October and build up during the second half of the month, and there is often a big arrival early in November with 4th–6th frequently significant. As with the fieldfare, persistent westerly winds with rain can delay this late autumn arrival until the third week of November.

Snow causes S–SW–W movement by most. Individuals which try to live through a cold spell often succumb.

Whitaker remarked that the redwing leaves before the fieldfare and TVBW records support this. Northerly movement has been observed as early as 13 February during the mild weather of an early spring. Most seem to pass through during March with the rearguard last noticed in early April. Hold-ups due to persistent easterly winds occur when flocks may be seen until well into April but, generally, only stragglers are recorded during the third week. Redwings in May are rare and 17 May is the latest date.

Dusky thrush Turdus naumanni Temminck
Rare vagrant.
   1 in 1905.

Ring ouzel Turdus torquatus Linnaeus
Rare passage migrant, irregular.
   3 winter records, 1901, Whitaker; 1942, 1960, TVBW.
   Perhaps because of its nocturnal movements, this summer visitor to the hills of Britain is only observed infrequently, in small numbers, in lowland Nottinghamshire, and then almost

invariably only a tired, grounded individual. Sometimes these stay several days before continuing their journey. Spring arrival has been recorded from 4 April to 9 May on dates which suggest that Continental birds are often involved. During the autumn birds have been seen from 3 September to 14 October. There is an isolated record for November by Sterland.

Blackbird Turdus merula Linnaeus
Abundant resident. Passage migrant and winter visitor.

As was mentioned earlier, this species is considered the most numerous on our farmland, although, if Nottinghamshire suffered a great loss of hedgerow, it could be replaced by the skylark. Bearing in mind that much of the county is of moist clay, the average density of the blackbird must be approximately 12 pairs per 100 acres, with favoured areas enjoying up to 16 pairs.

In our woodland it is numerous, especially on moist soils, and where grassland and woodland form a special ecological habitat such as the Gotham and West Leake Hills. Here the blackbird could have a density of 40 pairs per 100 acres, but it loses ground in less favourable places such as Rufford, where 11 pairs were found in 45 acres.

Its density in Grade 1 and 2 suburban habitats approximates to 35 pairs per 100 acres.

This species figures prominently on migration and other movements but, because of inability to differentiate from our own local blackbirds, migration is not well recorded. The Continental visitors (see chapter on Ringing) have an arrival and departure sequence very similar to that for both fieldfare and redwing. Parties arrive from September to early November, with a peak often in October when, at times, large flocks can be seen about our pastures and hawthorns. Young males are frequently dominant in numbers. Further arrival is noticeable when severe weather prevails elsewhere, and there is movement away from Nottinghamshire when snow persists.

Spring build-up and departure is the least documented of all and information is almost nil.

Wheatear   Oenanthe oenanthe (Linnaeus)

Fairly common passage migrant, most probably includes northern Europe and Greenland subspecies.

Formerly bred in small numbers, but only 1 record, in 1970, since 1948.

There are years when migrant wheatears are present in our county from March to October, and this is due to the presence of members of different races. Twice (and in recent years) very early wheatears have reached Nottinghamshire by 5 March, but the general arrival period is 22 March to 1 April. These sprightly leaders are usually spruce cock birds of the British race and they are quickly followed by the females. Sometimes this first wave of wheatears is very apparent, ending abruptly early in April, but more frequently the passage of the Continentals merges with it into general movement through the county north or north-eastwards. A third wave shows itself, if April is of normal temperature, and involves the larger, deeper-coloured Greenland race—from late April, but usually during May. This long spring movement ends during the third week of May, although stragglers occur into June, probably of birds destined for Greenland or northern Europe. Birds present during late June, eg from 25th to 30th, are a problem, and often it is impossible to tell whether such migrants are late spring to the north, or early summer to the south.

Excluding the late-June enigmas and, of course, the very occasional birds breeding locally, the first obvious wheatear migrants heading south appear around mid-July (6 times for the period 12–14 July), though only a few individuals. More regular migration sets in during the first week of August and continues until the third week of September. Except for occasional years when there is a fairly regular passage into October, probably of Continentals drifted across the North Sea, main movement ends in September, while October reports mark the stragglers; 29 October latest date for Nottinghamshire so far.

Stonechat   Saxicola torquata (Linnaeus)

Scarce winter visitor. Rare in summer, has bred very occasionally.

Ignoring the years when this species bred in Nottinghamshire, and excluding possible wanderers of British stock, there is left a small nucleus of winter visitors, considered to be of Continental origin. These birds arrive in the autumn, as early as September occasionally but more regularly during October. Severe wintry weather will force them to retreat SW/W. March is the month when they reappear or, if they have successfully wintered here, when they normally depart. The latest date on record for birds of passage is 18 April.

Winchat   Saxicola rubetra (Linnaeus)

Formerly fairly common summer visitor, but local, now uncommon.

In the 1920s and early 1930s, during the economic depression, some pasture land was neglected allowing intrusion by small hawthorns, and this type of habitat was used by small groups of whinchats. Pasture near Colston Bassett, grassland beside Green Lane, Bulcote, and below Ploughman's Wood, Woodborough, were examples of this 'rough' grassland. Since the war, modern farming has put paid to much of this whinchat habitat. Such rough grassland returned by accident when the raw earth around gravel pits became overgrown, allowing suitable breeding areas. Elsewhere the whinchat is a local bird of the open heathland and also of freshly planted forestry areas.

There is a record of a female of this species being seen on 22 February 1959. The observers had good views of it from as close as 5 yards, noting the buff eye-stripe and white in the tail. It must rank as one of the earliest on record for Britain and may have come rapidly north on a warm, southerly airstream which occurred at this time.

Normal early birds reach Nottinghamshire after the first week of April, from 13th onwards, and general arrival is, on average, during the fourth week of April into the first days of May. Cold springs can put back the entire arrival to May.

Observations have shown that local colonies of breeding birds begin to move out during the second half of July. Passage migrants are noted throughout August and the greatest gathering for early movement was of 64 birds in 1 field on 3 August 1946. The peak time is during the fourth week of August into early September, when influxes are sometimes considered to include Continental birds which have been drifted by easterly winds and grounded by unfavourable weather. Numbers fall off fairly rapidly and the last birds are regularly recorded during the fourth week of September. Only 3 exceptional late dates—6, 8 and 15 October.

Redstart   Phoenicurus phoenicurus (Linnaeus)
Fairly common summer visitor, but local. Some decrease since 1969.

Confined to the woodland of the light soils, especially on the Bunter Sandstone, it is of limited distribution (see map, page 187). Formerly much at home in the birch and oak complex, it is also breeding in conifer areas with an amenity or shelter fringe of deciduous trees, especially of birch. In Old Sherwood its density may match that of the marsh tit, say 4–6 pairs per 100 acres. Elsewhere it is probably 2–3 pairs where the habitat is suitable, and it is scarce to rare in most of the range shown.

The earliest date for a spring migrant of this species is 27 March, but the normal period for early arrivals is 6–9 April. General first arrivals, ie a number of birds in territory, are present 10–18 April and, of this period, the middle days of the month are significant. The vanguard of redstarts is always here during April, although really cold weather can delay it until the fourth week. Passage migration of northern birds continues well into May.

Departure of this secretive species from our breeding areas is difficult to witness, and yet in the vast area of the county where it does not breed it shows up well when on hedgerow passage. Movement has been recorded as early as 8 July, but passage in this month is small, it increases during August with more birds from the middle of the month until about the second week of September. Usually there is a slackening off after this and only stragglers continue into October. Influxes, in September especially,

REDSTART 1942-70
• Recorded breeding

are considered to include Continentals drifted west of their normal course. Exceptionally late birds were those of 6 November (1963) and 26 November (1970).

Black redstart   Phoenicurus ochruros (Gmelin)
Rare passage migrant, occasional.
Breeding proved 1958, 1963, 1964.

The earliest spring date is 31 March and birds have appeared in April on 3 occasions; while records for May are 2, on 8th and 11th.

Autumn passage dates are from 10 August with most during October to the 23rd. The Lace Market birds were last seen on 18 October having been present from June. Whitaker reported birds in Nottinghamshire from 10 to 23 December in 1857.

Nightingale   Luscinia megarhynchos Brehm
Scarce summer visitor, thinly distributed.

In 1911–12 a survey of the nightingale was carried out by
N. F. Ticehurst and Rev F. C. R. Jourdain, based on reports by
local observers. Their report was published in *British Birds* and
the findings for Nottinghamshire were:

> As compared with the adjoining county of Derbyshire, the distri-
> bution of the Nightingale is remarkable in extending far more to
> the north. But here again, as usual, the lie of the land gives the
> clue to the problem, for while the only low-lying parts of Derby-
> shire are the wide vale of the Trent and the lower parts of the
> Dove and Derwent valleys, all in the extreme south of the county,
> the greater part of Nottinghamshire is traversed by the Trent,
> with low-lying meadows on either side as it flows northward to
> the Humber, and the only rising ground is in the Mansfield dis-
> trict, while even here only one or two scattered portions exceed
> 600 feet in height. So that it is not surprising to find that there are
> few districts in which it has not occasionally bred, while it is quite
> common in the Trent Valley between Nottingham and Newark,
> as well as on the Leicestershire border near Belvoir. In the Trent
> Valley above Nottingham it is much scarcer, but has bred for three
> or four years past, at any rate, at Wollaton (Miss M. Russell),
> while Mr. C. E. Pearson heard it only twice in thirty years at
> Chilwell. Lower down it is much commoner, and is reported at three
> places between Nottingham and Lowdham (Mr. C. E. Pearson),
> at Arnold, Oxton and Southwell, the two latter regularly (Mr. J.
> Whitaker), at Bleasby (Miss N. Marsh), while Mr. Poynty Wright
> has found it plentiful in the Trent Valley as far as Newark, and
> thinks that it shows a tendency to increase. He also considers it
> fairly well distributed in the south-east corner of the county, and
> it is common in the Vale of Belvoir, and breeds there (Whatton-
> in-the-Vale, etc.). In the Sherwood Forest district it is only an
> occasional visitor, and Mr. Whitaker only records it five times in
> thirty-four years at Rainworth, but states that it has nested at
> Ollerton. Still further north we come to the well-wooded and
> fertile 'Dukeries'. Here a few pairs have long been known to breed
> near Worksop, and the Rev. L. C. Barnes heard two in song in
> May, 1909 at Scofton, while Mr. Whitaker states that it has nested
> near Retford. From the north-east of the county our information
> is defective, but it is probable that a few pairs breed there also.

From 1935 TVBW records show a similar result, with good and poor years plus a tendency for a pair or two to appear in an area (as at Rainworth in the 1911–12 report) for a year or two only to disappear again. These two aspects are probably due to the vagaries and hazards of migration, to good or bad breeding seasons, and to the fact that our county is at the extreme north-western end of the nightingale's range.

In addition to the areas already mentioned this species was always well established in the Ossington area and other woods of the central Keuper, some were close to Bawtry, and others on the Lincolnshire border. There is now some apprehension over the change to conifers in many of its established breeding woods.

The nightingale in peak years probably comes in the 50–100 pairs bracket for the whole county with the Dukeries probably having the greatest concentration. Normally, it must be at or below 50 pairs.

The bird is unobtrusive by habit both on the ground and on migration. Its ability to travel incognito and to get to its destination with a minimum of fuss makes it a difficult bird to assess for movement. The recording of arrival dates is almost invariably due to its incomparable voice, which means that the actual day of arrival is not always known.

Whitaker made no records of arrival time and the following is based solely on the TVBW years of 1942–70. There is one outstandingly early date, 10 April 1961, and 4 others come within the period 15–18 April. With the exception of 2 years when the first were in May, all other first dates are within the period 20–29 April, with 20th–22nd the general time for first arrivals when the weather is average. Further arrival and build-up is usual for the fourth week of April and continues into May some years.

Information on departure is almost nil. It is known that birds are present into July and there is only one other date, 5 August, when a juvenile was seen in Clumber Park.

Robin   Erithacus rubecula (Linnaeus)
Common resident, and probably passage migrant at times.

On true farmland, ie with a minimum of woodland, the robin

only holds a minor position at around 2–4 pairs to the 100 acres. In contrast, it is placed as the commonest species for the deciduous and mixed woods, with a density of at or around 40 pairs per 100 acres. It is one of the few species which manages to breed in the conifer plantations, although there are far less in this habitat.

Familiar enough about suburban gardens during the winter, the robin is not numerous in this habitat as a breeding bird, and its density in the Grade 2 areas is assessed at 1 pair per 100 acres.

Grasshopper warbler   Locustella naevia (Boddaert)
Uncommon winter visitor.

From Whitaker down the years to TVBW times of World War II, this bird was considered to be widespread but local, a species which came to Nottinghamshire in small numbers. It is not common now and yet more are reported, which could mean an increase in numbers, although more likely to be an increase in observers, now much more mobile. However, with the development of the forestry plantations it can be definitely claimed to have increased in those areas. Nowhere is it dense enough to hold any important position numerically. Under ideal conditions a forest area can hold territories for several pairs in fairly close proximity.

Although as furtive as the nightingale, this bird will indulge in hedgerow passage and sing while on the move, thereby attracting attention to become a statistic in a notebook. A few individuals have been referred to as 'tame'.

TVBW have only 3 early dates—4 April for 1943 and 1961, and 8 April for 1944. Nearly all other first arrivals are from 17 April into the fourth week, with the period 17–18 April fairly frequent. This species comes in well and the main arrival usually takes place very quickly after the first birds have arrived. Build-up and through movement continue into May during late springs.

Departure is not so well documented. Song from birds in territory is fairly regular during July, especially for the first half of the month, and song in territory in August has been reported several times. Birds on passage will sing however. A known breeding area holding a number of pairs became deserted by 23 July one year.

Birds out of territory and on hedgerow passage have been recorded as early as 14 July. Departure, therefore, seems to begin during the second half of July, and continues through August, with the rearguard few in early September. Latest date 13 September.

Reed warbler   Acrocephalus scirpaceus (Hermann)
Uncommon summer visitor, local.

This species is local in distribution due to its preference for the common reed (Phragmites communis) which, although widespread throughout our county, does not always grow densely enough for nesting. Consequently, the distribution of the reed warbler is as patchy as are the patches of suitable reed! An elusive and yet quite noisy bird, which occurs throughout the county, with an isolated pair or small group here and there beside lake, stream, canal or other strip of boggy fen. Sunken willow holts and subsidence marshes have been used in the past, with a few pairs using young osiers, the stems of the greater willow herb and even the dog rose for the nest site.

The only area where this species has been studied intensively is the Attenborough Nature Reserve, which became a field-study centre for undergraduates from Nottingham University who have produced a number of papers on the Acrocephalus species (Dr Kent and Messrs Bell, Catchpole and Hornby); the population there was approximately 63 pairs in 1966.

The two earliest spring dates are 16 and 19 April. The normal time for early individuals to appear is during the fourth week of April. Very occasionally good numbers have come in by the end of this month but, for most years, general arrival is during May, especially in the first 2 weeks.

Although difficult to record, there is evidence of some departure during the second half of July. General movement is during August and into early September, leaving very small numbers until the fourth week. Really late birds are into October, usually to the 6th, but there is one later date, 19th.

Marsh warbler   Acrocephalus palustris (Bechstein)
Rare summer visitor.
2 definite records, 1969 (when breeding was proved), 1972.

Sedge warbler   Acrocephalus schoenobaenus (Linnaeus)
Common summer visitor.

Less confined by choice of nest site, this Acrocephalus warbler is common and widespread. Attenborough was found to hold at least 65 pairs in 1968 in this extensive and ideal area whereas, elsewhere, the number of birds breeding almost colonially is related to the amount of suitable habitat. Surveys of the dykeland in the Carrland found the sedge warbler to be very numerous.

The earliest ever to arrive in Nottinghamshire was on 8 April which, with the next 4 days, marks the period of the very early birds. The usual time for early birds is 14–20 April. Whitaker found that they arrived mainly during the fourth week of April and TVBW records show that this is the week for the first good numbers. Major arrival can take place at this time in warm weather, but the pleasant, dramatic large-scale appearance of this species is often delayed until early May. Further through migration frequently continues into the second week.

Sedge warblers begin to move south from mid-July and numbers increase into August, although young of late nests are still being fed to mid-August. After early September there is a rapid decrease and, most years, the last birds are seen during the third week or just into the fourth. Very late stragglers are present now and then into early October. Latest date 7 October.

Icterine warbler   Hippolais icterina (Vieillot)
Rare vagrant.
1 in 1945.

Blackcap   Sylvia atricapilla (Linnaeus)
Fairly common summer visitor. Rare winter visitor, most years since 1950.

The blackcap is a fairly important member of the woodland

community and it proclaims this by its attractive and loud silvery song. Because it can manage with even a small roadside fringe of a wood, or a deciduous edge to a conifer plantation, as well as the better habitats, it usually figures in the lists of counts made at any wooded area. Density is from 10–12 pairs per 100 acres.

Because of this species' ability to winter in England it is possible that March birds are among those which did not migrate. However, the 2 birds in Wollaton Park on 30 March 1957 could have been genuine arrivals, especially as it was an exceptionally mild March with other early migrants arriving. Normal first individuals appear 5–12 April, first small numbers from then until the 16th, general arrival from the 17th, and into May in cold springs.

Southward movement gets underway around the middle of July, when some males are still singing in their territories. Momentum increases from late July with migration continuing throughout August. Last numbers are seen during the first half of September, but by then this species is scarce and it is thought that these late birds are from northern areas or even the Continent. The final few occur at times during October. Later dates are classed as wintering.

Barred warbler   Sylvia nisoria (Bechstein)
Rare vagrant.
   1 in 1968.

Garden warbler   Sylvia borin (Boddaert)
Uncommon summer visitor.

In Nottinghamshire this warbler is of widespread distribution but nowhere is it densely situated. The blackcap outnumbers it by far, possibly by 4 to 1, and it is one of the scarcer regulars to our woodland. This robust bird, judging from the paucity of migratory observations, does not indulge in hedgerow (or ground) movement as much as some of the other warblers. It must, literally, drop from the sky!

Except for two dates on 7 April (out of 11 years recorded) Whitaker found it tended to arrive in May.

TVBW records from 1942 yield one exceptionally early date, 29 March (this was in 1969 when 2 other early individuals were also recorded and when the local population was in territory before the end of April). Until this March record the earliest was 6 April (1946) and 7 April (1961). The normal period for the early ones is 13–20 April and general influx is during the fourth week of April into May, till the third week during backward springs or because of adverse winds.

Southward movement begins around mid-July increasing into August with the period 15 August to 10 September as the peak time for departure. The last, occasional, birds are seen into the first week of October.

The very late dates of 28 November (1961) and 4 and 20 December (1969) probably come under the heading of wintering.

Whitethroat   Sylvia communis Latham
Common summer visitor until 1969, when there was a population crash, and it became scarce. Recovery has been slow and at 1973 it is still incomplete.

The common whitethroat ('Peggy' or 'nettlecreeper' are its Nottinghamshire names) is the main warbler of the open farm-land, being found at the laneside or well in the hinterland where few people walk. Given a short, thick hedge or a tangled ditch it is quite at home, and from 2–4 pairs per 100 acres is a fair average when numbers are normal.

It is a bird of the woodland edge or the more open aspects, and could be classed as a fringe species. Therefore, as it will not be found in the main stands of trees, it will not occupy an important position. Where it does occur, however, it must be in the region of 4–8 pairs per 100 acres according to the suitability of the habitat.

The earliest date is 5 April. Very early arrivals before 11 April are rare, and the vanguard usually appears during the second week of April. General arrival begins in the third week, weather per-mitting, but is frequently from 22 April into May. Sometimes occupation of territories is delayed until the second week of May.

Records show that movement becomes apparent from 24 July, although it could be a little earlier, and frequently a peak has occurred during the first 2 weeks of August. Passage of grounded birds is steady with the middle of September the extreme limit. Afterwards a small rearguard is present until the fourth week with rare, late birds into October to the second week.

An exceptional winter bird was caught and ringed at Attenborough on 10 December 1966. Also there was a bird with an injured wing, January 1972.

Lesser whitethroat *Sylvia curruca* (*Linnaeus*)
Scarce summer visitor, thinly distributed.

Sterland considered it to be almost as common as the preceding species around Ollerton. Whitaker reported it as less common and more local. The TVBW cover from 1935 has never really got to grips with the status of the lesser whitethroat. Of course, it has figured prominently in records which show a wide yet thin distribution. There is a possibility of its being overlooked but, nevertheless, it ranks as being much less numerous than the common whitethroat. Where it does occur there are usually tall hawthorns, hedgerow trees and, according to some birdwatchers, a little water. It is not a species which will be found on a farm of small neat hedgerows.

An early bird was once recorded on 16 April and any observed from 16–21 April are exceptionally early. Usual first arrivals are during the fourth week of April, but often the main and entire arrival can be during May.

Departure probably starts around mid-July, and generally birds become obvious from late July, with August and early September the main movement period. There is a sharp decrease in observations afterwards, with last records during the third week of September. Latest date is 22 September.

Willow warbler *Phylloscopus trochilus* (*Linnaeus*)
Common summer visitor.

Happily a numerous species everywhere, this summer visitor,

because of its numbers, contributes greatly to the spring chorus. It is close to the blue tit and the wren in numbers with a density in the best habitats of 25–35 pairs per 100 acres.

The five earliest birds were 8, 14 and 21 March (TVBW) and 16 and 20 March (Whitaker). These could have been birds which had wintered north of their range, perhaps with the chiffchaffs, and so were able to have a good start, although it is possible that they were eager leaders from normal winter quarters.

The usual very early birds appear during the fourth week of March or during the first few days of April. Discussion on the arrival of this species for the years 1954 to 1963 (TVBW annual report, 1964) showed that the main arrival is closely connected with the movement north of the 48° F (9° C) isotherm which is, on average, during the period 11–20 April.

The willow warbler is a favourite migrant of the birdwatcher because it will travel during the day at low level, sometimes in loose groups, and also it attracts attention by singing.

In cold northerly winds the main arrival can be delayed and the passage of northern birds through Nottinghamshire can be witnessed well into May. Most appear to travel due north or north-east.

Southward movement has been recorded as early as 10 July. General departure, however, is from the end of the third week of July, with August the main month for seeing good numbers, and records support the view that there is often a peak during the first 10 days of August.

Just as the sight of northward-moving groups is a feature of spring migration, the discovery of a loose 'flock' of up to 30 birds in association with other species is a sign of migrational trouble in August or early September. It is considered that these birds have been grounded by cloud or rain and their very active feeding in these circumstances is thought to be replacing lost migrational fat.

After the middle of September willow warblers decrease drastically, and often the last sighting is during the fourth week. Stragglers after the first week of October are rare. Latest date 3 November.

Chiffchaff Phylloscopus collybita (Vieillot)
Common summer visitor. Occasional winter, November–January.

In Nottinghamshire the chiffchaff is confined to the mature trees in the main and therefore has less variety of habitat than the willow warbler. Its density must be about a third, from 8–10 pairs per 100 acres.

In 1882 Whitaker shot a chiffchaff on 28 February to prove his earliest arrival date. This remained the earliest for Nottinghamshire until 1949 when one was recorded on 14 February. Both these birds could have been individuals which had wintered in southern England or well north of their winter range.

A study of the arrival of the willow warbler and the chiffchaff for the years 1954–63 (Dobbs and Lamb, TVBW annual report, 1964) showed that the chiffchaff seemed to arrive with the 45° F (7° C) isotherm, although there could be early or late years according to the prevailing weather system.

Whitaker's first dates for 34 of the years from 1871 to 1906 showed early individuals 13–14 March; first dates for 16 of the years were 20–31 March, and most of the others were by 11 April. TVBW records from 1942 to 1970 closely support this, with very early birds 5–18 March, early birds from 20 March and general arrival of first birds (males?) during the fourth week of March. Exceptional spells of warm south-west winds can cause the total arrival of our local chiffchaffs to be completed before the end of March (eg 1957), but generally the main arrival of good numbers was during the first 10 or 11 days of April. Adverse weather, naturally, can retard arrival.

Departure begins in July, recorded as early as the 12th, and gains momentum during August when, perhaps, British stock is mainly involved. Good numbers can be recorded during September when, possibly, our woods are temporarily filled with Continental birds. This influx is dependent on the vagaries of the weather, and some years there are few records for September. The last birds are seen or heard (quiet farewell arias!) during the first 12 days of October, and the latest, exceptional, date is 29 October.

The sprinkling of November, December and January dates concern wintering birds.

Wood warbler   Phylloscopus sibilatrix (Bechstein)
Scarce passage migrant. Occasional summer visitor.
Arrival of this scarce species has been as early as 3 April (Whitaker) and 10 April (TVBW). However, the date charts show marked arrival during the fourth week of April until 12 May. The continued passage after this date has on a few occasions continued into the middle of June.

Ringing at Toton before the ridge was built over showed good southward movement in 1957 from mid-July to 4 August when 18 birds were caught. Other TVBW records show movement from 15 July continuing through August and with a few laggards to 18 September.

Yellow-browed warbler   Phylloscopus inornatus (Blyth)
Rare vagrant.
1, 18 October 1914. This bird was well seen by C. E. Pearson, the experienced ornithologist at Lowdham, and in view of present knowledge (eg, that 15–21 October is a regular time for east-coast arrivals in the central England areas) the record is considered a good one.

Goldcrest   Regulus regulus (Linnaeus)
Fairly common resident and winter visitor. More widely distributed out of the breeding season.
Because it is almost a complete conifer species using forestry plantations, mixed woods, big gardens, churchyards where evergreen trees grow, the goldcrest is missing from many of our woods. Density is most probably at 2–4 pairs per 100 acres.

The presence of our own stock obscures the arrival of the winter visitors. This has taken place as early as mid-September but records reveal that main arrival is usually during October, and it is during this month that exhausted or dying birds are found in strange places, eg in a school or a city-centre car park.

Records are even less sensitive for the spring departure of these visitors, but on occasions, usually during adverse weather hold-ups, we have gained an insight into this east–north-east movement which can take place during March and to the middle of April.

Firecrest Regulus ignicapillus (Temminck)
Rare vagrant/winter visitor.
   9 records, 1850, c 1878, 1907 (Whitaker); 1946, 1950, 1952, 1958, 1968, 1972 (TVBW).

Spotted flycatcher Muscicapa striata (Pallas)
Fairly common summer visitor.
   Density in our woods is about 4 pairs per 100 acres. Familiar also in gardens and churchyards with plenty of trees.
   For 64 of the years reviewed from 1871 this unobtrusive summer visitor was first seen in April on only 8 occasions (earliest 20 April 1948 and 1950) and, as Whitaker pointed out, it consistently arrives in May. It comes more often in the second week of May than the first, and arrival has fairly often been delayed until June.
   As with most of the summer visitors, southward migration is a long-drawn-out affair. The first few can be noticed from mid-July and the main exodus is during August into early September. Some years there is quite a fall of this species, eg 40 in a loose gathering at Cotgrave on 25 August 1959, while groups of 10–20 are fairly frequent. In most years the last are seen during the final fortnight of September, and there are only 3 dates for October; latest date 7 October.

Pied flycatcher Ficedula hypoleuca (Pallas)
Rare passage migrant.
   Said to have bred twice (Whitaker).
   When one considers the good numbers seen on the east coast during migration times, it is surprising how few are recorded in Nottinghamshire, and possibly it is overlooked.

The inclusive dates for the northward trek (TVBW 1942–70) are from 2 April to 10 June and, in this period, there are concentrations of sightings for the fourth week of April and around the middle of May. The autumn movement has an early date of 26 July, most birds following during August with a few to 11 September, and there is 1 isolated record for 13 October.

Red-breasted flycatcher   Ficedula parva (Bechstein)
Rare vagrant.

2 records, 1947, 1950.

Dunnock   Prunella modularis (Linnaeus)
Abundant resident.

Unlike the wren and the robin, the dunnock (or hedge sparrow) has taken advantage of the field hedgerow (trim, low ones for preference) and has prospered in this habitat. From 8–12 pairs per 100 acres covers the density of this bird in the farmland habitat.

In woodland its numbers are quite high and its density could be as great as 25–30 pairs per 100 acres, although it is a very difficult species to assess in areas of thick cover.

As a suburban bird of the Grade 2 areas it could be slightly more numerous than the blackbird, at a density of 35 pairs to 100 acres, but it is probably less able to use the suburbs with smaller gardens.

To a great extent this is a sedentary species, and yet movement south-west or west along the Trent Valley has been noticed on occasions between 20 September and 3 October.

Meadow pipit   Anthus pratensis (Linnaeus)
Fairly common resident. Common passage migrant and winter visitor.

During the depression in farming, when much land was under grass and there was a maximum of rough pasture, this species was frequently found in loose colonies in such places. It still breeds with us there but numbers are much less because of the increase in arable and the improved, tidy conditions. To some extent there has been a shift of locality and it is found where wasteland and rough grassland exist, such as the grassy floodbanks and the gravel-pit perimeters.

This species probably marks the end of winter more than any other for, as soon as there is a hint of spring in the air, flocks moving north appear. The main period, from TVBW records, is mid-March to late April, with influxes regular between late March and 15 April. Delayed birds into May have been observed.

There is reference to slight movement south from the end of July. Traditionally, however, the meadow pipit crosses Nottinghamshire to more southern areas during September and October. In some years the last of this movement takes place in early November. Birds wintering with us are subject to hard-weather movement.

Richard's pipit   Anthus novaeseelandiae (Gmelin)
Rare vagrant.
   1 in 1971.

Tree pipit   Anthus trivialis (Linnaeus)
Fairly common summer visitor, formerly common and more widespread.

Found on the open areas of woodland and in parkland, the distribution of this species has altered during the last 30 years due mainly to the ploughing up of permanent grassland and the felling of trees. Rare now in the main farming areas, it is still to be found wherever forestry provides suitable habitat in the form of a cleared plantation, a burnt-out area, where the birch-scrub type of heathland prevails, and in a few isolated corners. In public-access areas it suffers from the pressure of visitors and their dogs. Because of its localised habitat it does not hold a high place numerically, and has been reduced in status from 'common' to 'fairly common' in forest country since 1960 at least.

The earliest arrival date is 30 March. Whitaker considered it most consistent in arriving during April and, in 31 years of recording from 1875, only twice did he first observe the tree pipit after April. A summary for 60 years shows only 1 March record (as above), and only 5 years when the first one came in the period 3–9 April; general time for first arrivals was 10–17 April. The usual time for the main influx was during the third and fourth weeks of April.

Desertion of breeding areas has been recorded by 28 July and during August. There have been few September reports of passage birds and the last, isolated date is 22 October.

Rock pipit   Anthus spinoletta petrosus (Montagu)
Rare passage migrant. Some Scandinavian (*A. s. littoralis*).

Considered by some local ornithologists to be overlooked, the rock pipit has been recorded at various gravel pits, industrial flashes and, not surprisingly, beside the River Trent where stone has been used to prevent bank erosion. It was often seen on the old Nottingham Sewage Farm. Whitaker and Sterland did not record it.

The inclusive autumn migration dates are 6 October to 26 November, and the spring dates 17 March to 4 April.

Water pipit   Anthus spinoletta spinoletta (Linnaeus)
Rare winter visitor. Recorded in only 8 winters from 1944, but probably overlooked.

This mountain sub-species of rock pipit was considered to be an extremely occasional visitor to Nottinghamshire until recent years, when evidence was obtained of 1 or 2 individuals appearing each winter in the upper reaches of the River Erewash and at suitable wet places, sewage tanks and flashes on each side of the Nottinghamshire–Derbyshire border.

Inclusive dates are from 6 September to 1 April.

Pied wagtail   Motacilla alba yarrellii (Gould)
Common resident and passage migrant.

During the breeding season this species is very evident as it leads its active life around our farms and villages, alongside the roadside streams, or at and near other waters. From July onwards numbers congregate in the river valleys wherever water holds plenty of insects. To the practised eye the winter roost flights to some snug spot, which may be reeds or other aquatic vegetation, cosy rhododendrons or even factory ventilators, are as obvious as the dusk flights of starling and gull. The pied wagtail is a great follower of the plough and now, in these days of winter fishing-matches, is a beggar at the maggot tins.

Passage movements northwards in the spring have been observed from the middle of March into early April. Dispersal movement has been recorded as early as mid-July, but more general movement usually begins in August continuing into September, with good numbers fairly frequent in October.

White wagtail *Motacilla alba alba Linnaeus*
Scarce passage migrant.

The Continental pied wagtail is regular at the edges of our various waters. Most are recorded at our gravel pits, but there must be some bias here in connection with the local birdwatcher and his preference of an area for a morning out!

The inclusive dates are 25 March to 26 May for the spring migration, with April the peak time, and 9 August to 27 October for the few on autumn passage.

Grey wagtail *Motacilla cinerea Tunstall*
Uncommon winter visitor and passage migrant. Rare and occasional in summer. Breeding first proved 1955, but doubtless overlooked before then.

The grey wagtails which breed occasionally are probably an offshoot of full populations from the hill country of Derbyshire. Significantly, after several years without any breeding-season reports following this species' decline, especially after the 1962-3 winter, birds are appearing again just at a time when the hill territories must be fully occupied. It is not surprising to find that the streams of the north-west around Moorgreen and Sutton-in-Ashfield have been used. Further inside Nottinghamshire, pairs have bred beside the River Leen and the Dover Beck where flow and suitable nest sites were available.

After the breeding season small numbers appear during July and August, probably part of early dispersal from Derbyshire or Yorkshire. There is an increase in September, with October and November often the peak months. By the end of the year numbers fall to a static winter population which can be very small; some find a good living in the city centre instead of about our various waters.

There can be a slight increase in early spring. It is considered that birds from the northern half of Britain are involved although, as some are observed moving with the passage of redwings, fieldfares and others, some may be of Continental origin.

Yellow wagtail   Motacilla flava flavissima (Blyth)
Common summer visitor and passage migrant.

To find this attractive summer visitor it is necessary to visit one of our vales or river valleys and, although it will nest in arable crops, it is really a bird of the pastures. Numerically, it is a minor member of any farm's bird-life.

This species shows considerable variation in peak arrival and departure times. First arrivals can occur in March (earliest, 23rd), but the normal period is during the first week of April. This arrival of first males can be delayed to 12–15 April if the weather is unsuitable, whereas during warmer springs the middle of April marks the arrival of good numbers. The second half of this month is a time of good arrival and passage and, some years, marked movement (females mentioned at times) continues into early May.

Departure is long-lasting, beginning in early July and continuing into October. In 1968 local birds began to leave as early as 5 July and a peak departure period was from late July into the first week of August; in contrast, there are years when the main movement is in late August to near the end of September. An average year could be summarised: small numbers migrating in July, increase with peaks in August into early September followed by a rapid decrease, and finally a few stragglers into October.

There are 2 November records—8th and 10th.

Blue-headed wagtail   Motacilla flava flava Linnaeus
Rare passage migrant.

The few wagtails of the true flava race appear especially at times of easterly or south-easterly winds. The inclusive dates of these are 19 April to 7 June with most from the end of April into May, and in the autumn from 26 July to 6 September.

> *Flava sp   As well as records of Motacilla f. flava,* there are
> others of hybrids (flava/flavissima) or of yellow wagtail
> showing some of the characteristcs of blue-headed. Rare
> and irregular.

Waxwing   Bombycilla garrulus (Linnaeus)
Scarce/rare winter visitor, irregular.

The earliest arrival date of this irruptive species is 10 October. Most first arrivals appear in November. January to March is the period when the waxwing has appeared most frequently as a winter wanderer from other areas of Great Britain. There are 3 dates for April, the last 29th.

1 seen 18–19 August 1971 was thought to be a 'left-over' from the previous winter rather than an early migrant.

Great grey shrike   Lanius excubitor Linnaeus
Rare winter visitor, most years 1961–73.

Inclusive dates for Nottinghamshire are 15 October to 14 April.

Woodchat shrike   Lanius senator Linnaeus
Rare vagrant.

1 in 1859 (Whitaker).

Red-backed shrike   Lanius collurio Linnaeus
Rare passage migrant, occasional. Formerly summer visitor, probably rare, and last breeding 1947.

Starling   Sturnus vulgaris Linnaeus
Abundant resident and winter visitor.

The starling is a field species and its requirements are satisfied by the average farm, where it will be found at approximately 3–4 pairs per 100 acres. Breeding pairs are probably regulated by the number of nest sites available as, usually, there are a number of non-breeding birds also present in the fields.

Any woodland possessing old woodpecker holes or cavities in aged trees will have almost as many pairs of starlings as there are holes. That is the key to its density in woodland surrounded by farmland. It is an obvious species at woodland during the winter due to the huge roosts. Dense pole-stage conifers, which are snug, are preferred. Trees are damaged and the birds always introduce elder scrub.

Most country people are aware of the great winter flocks of this species which are due to the Continental visitors. Some have been detected arriving from 21 September, but October is the main month for arrival and through movements in Nottinghamshire, the last birds occurring during the first half of November.

There are hard-weather movements although, often, severe wintry weather merely causes a change in the pattern of roost flights, when field flocks spend their day in the built-up areas instead of in open country.

Departure can start in February and during a period of mild weather this exodus can be considerable. However, March is the main month for the great return to Europe and the last go during April, especially, if the winter lingers locally beyond the calendar date of 20 March.

Rose-coloured starling   Sturnus roseus (Linnaeus)
Rare vagrant.

1, undated, and 1856 (Whitaker); exceptional series of records, 1945–51, involving 25 birds, 1958, 1959.

Hawfinch   Coccothraustes coccothraustes (Linnaeus)
Scarce resident, local.

This species was rare during the middle of the 19th century, but Whitaker thought that it was on its way to becoming fairly common by 1906. The hawfinch seems to prefer life in loose colonies and anyone living in a favoured area could be excused in thinking that this bird was similarly distributed elsewhere in the county. TVBW records show that it has remained constant in the deciduous woods of the Dukeries forest country and the maximum is probably 30 pairs. South of Nottingham there has always been a colony of around 10 pairs (perhaps more at peak times) while, at one time, the Colwick Woods held up to 11 pairs.

Elsewhere, especially in farmland woods, the hawfinch is rarely seen, but this could be partly due to its elusive nature. A round estimate for this species when the population is not affected by winter losses or food shortages would be about 60 pairs for Nottinghamshire.

Greenfinch   Carduelis chloris (Linnaeus)
Common resident.

This species nests in the field hedges and usually prefers those of 8 feet or more. It is generally distributed over the farmland habitat, but is never numerous, averaging 2–3 pairs per 100 acres.

Close contact with this species suggests that it is not very intelligent: however, as it is obviously successful in a variety of habitats, including woodland, this conception must be wrong. Density differs according to the type of wood and the type of surroundings, and is probably from 4–8 pairs per 100 acres. The greenfinch requires bushes and shrubs preferably near the outer edge of a wood, and nearby there should be good feeding areas.

In suburbia, areas Grade 1 and 2, it is probably at 3 pairs per 100 acres.

This species has not been seen to be involved in migration movements, and even though a little movement has been detected during autumn arrival times, the comings and goings of the visitors have been lost among the short journeys of the largely sedentary local population.

Goldfinch *Carduelis carduelis* (*Linnaeus*)

Common resident. Considerable increase since 1940.

Farmland goldfinches are not numerous and the hedgerow-field habitat is probably only a secondary preference. An assessment of 1 pair per 100 acres is probably too high a density.

This species, also, is not a true forest bird, and it belongs to the orchards, the churchyard trees, and the varied habitats of the open country. It is sometimes found nesting in woodland, where a tree on the outer edge is often used .Whitaker considered it not very plentiful and cites only 2 nests for his home area. It is at a density of 4 pairs per 100 acres as a woodland-fringe bird and as a member of gardens, allotments and small-holdings with plenty of trees.

In Grade 1 and 2 areas of the built-up zones it is placed at 1–2 pairs per 100 acres.

During late summer and into early autumn, flocks of goldfinches add colour and music to the weedy wastelands. These birds are combined family groups which disappear, presumably to the south, before the onset of winter. Goldfinches are far fewer then, and some of these wintering birds, from their duller body colouring and stronger red on their faces, are thought to be Continentals.

In early spring there is a noticeable return of the local birds which become obvious almost dramatically at the lane-side and about the gardens.

Siskin *Carduelis spinus* (*Linnaeus*)

Uncommon winter visitor. Occasional influxes of flocks of up to 200 birds. First garden reports of birds at peanuts, 1973.

The inclusive dates of this winter visitor are 17 September to 29 April. Early arrivals come during the second half of September some years, and the main arrival is during October. Occasionally last dates in the spring are in March, but usually during the third and fourth weeks of April.

Linnet Acanthis cannabina (Linnaeus)
Common resident. Some emigrate for the winter to Mediterranean areas.

This small finch has adapted itself well to the farmland type of
country. In early April the flocks of tuneful linnets are a feature
of the young spring before they split up into pairs and commence
nesting in the field hedgerows, often in loose colonies. Small
hedges up to 3–4 feet are preferred. At 4–7 pairs per 100 acres,
the linnet ranks as one of the successful farm birds.

It is also a common bird of the open areas of the forest country,
finding such habitats as the heathland of gorse and birch, the
young plantations of deciduous and coniferous trees and the scrub
very suitable; it is considered to be more numerous here than on
the farm land. Density is thought to be from 8–10 pairs per 100
acres.

Movements by this species are not always clear. Large flocks
gather during August and September and movement to the
south-west has been observed. The percentage of local birds
which migrate is not known. The wintering linnets are thought
to come from north of Nottinghamshire and perhaps from
Europe. Just occasionally, an exodus and an influx have been
detected during the spring, suggesting a changeover of the
different populations.

Twite Acanhis flavirostris (Linnaeus)
Rare winter visitor, irregular.

Inclusive dates are from 1 September to 30 March and, although
this species has been observed in all the winter months, most
have been seen in December and March.

Redpoll Acanthis flammea cabaret (Muller)
Fairly common resident from 1960s. Fairly common winter
visitor, sometimes with flocks of up to 100 birds, 'forest' country.
Uncommon in more open country.

Sterland and Whitaker were familiar with this small finch as a
breeding species and, although not as common as the linnet, it

was not considered to be rare or even in small numbers. Whitaker remarked that it was found more often in central and northern areas of the county.

During the recording years of the TVBW it was known as a scarce resident, with most concentrated in the forest country, until the 1960s, when it became a widespread and fairly common breeding species in all our softwood areas. It also appeared in other areas such as our deciduous woods and uncultivated land with trees.

Because this sudden increase is recent there has not been enough accumulation of data to assess density. Places such as the Stapleford Woods, Cotgrave Forest, Kirklington Woods, Manor Hills, near Worksop, Clumber Park, and the West Leake and Gotham Hills, are known to hold something from 4–10 pairs. In the Birklands the breeding stock is assessed as 'in good numbers'. Post-breeding flocks, before the arrival of the winter visitors, have numbered from 30–100 birds in the areas named.

The winter visitors from northern Britain and the Continent begin to arrive during the third week of September, more generally during October and, at times, the main influx can be later. The large flocks, usually in the Dukeries, gradually diminish from the third week of March while, during late springs, groups remain into May.

Mealy redpoll   Acanthis flammea flammea (Linnaeus)
Rare vagrant.

1848, 1946, 1968, 1969, 1973, but most probably overlooked.

Bullfinch   Pyrrhula pyrrhula (Linnaeus)
Fairly common resident. Increased during the late 1950s–1966.

It is not numerous on farmland and is probably similar to the goldfinch, with a status of about one pair to 100–200 acres. Familiar enough to all who quietly walk the Nottinghamshire woods and thickets, the bullfinch has a density of from 4–6 pairs per 100 acres.

Pine grosbeak   Pinicola enucleator (Linnaeus)
Rare vagrant.
    2 in 1890.

Crossbill   Loxia curvirostra (Linnaeus)
Scarce visitor, irregular, occasional irruptions starting mid-summer. Considered to have bred at times, but only positive 1967 and 1973.
    The inclusive dates for arrival are from 26 June into August, although further arrival can occur in September. After winter wandering, departure often occurs in March with late birds to 24 April.
    Big summer irruptions sometimes cause birds to 'settle' when breeding takes place and, consequently, groups are seen during the year following the irruption.

Parrot crossbill   Loxia pityopsittacus Borkhausen
Rare vagrant.
    2 records, 1848 (Felkin), but given as 1849 by Whitaker; 1963.

Two-barred crossbill   Loxia leucoptera Gmelin
Rare vagrant.
    2 records, 1875, 1943.

Chaffinch   Fringilla coelebs Linnaeus
Common resident, passage migrant and winter visitor.
    The chaffinch is very much a bird of the woodlands, and yet it has found the farmland a suitable habitat, thanks to the hawthorn hedge which, incidentally, must be taller than that required by whitethroat and linnet. Formerly quite numerous and, therefore, common along the laneside, this species suffered a decline associated with the toxic seed-dressing years 1959–61 followed by losses during the 1962–3 winter. There has been some recovery since and, at the beginning of the 1970s, density on typical farmland without too much woodland would be 4–8 pairs per 100 acres.

One of the dominant species in woodland, the chaffinch makes this known in early spring when it vies with robin and blackbird for the role of chief songster before the summer species arrive to diversify the chorus. Rowlands with 27 pairs in 50 acres, and Spencer with 15 pairs in 45 acres, reveal the high density which can be achieved. Taking the county as a whole this species probably has a density similar to the dunnock at 25–30 pairs per 100 acres.

Autumn migration and arrival has been recorded from 20 September. October is the main arrival month with good numbers at times into early November, and last movement to 20 November. Hard-weather movements take place during the winter. Spring migration does not show up well visually and only late March figures in the records.

Brambling *Fringilla montifringilla* Linnaeus
Uncommon winter visitor, but up to 1,000 birds occasionally during influxes. Summer birds have occurred, but exceedingly rare.

The earliest autumn date is 20 September but, on average, the early birds are seen during the first week of October, and the general arrival is from the middle of the month. Departure can take place late in March, but mainly in April. Latest date is 6 May, excluding the very rare summering birds.

Yellowhammer *Emberiza citrinella* Linnaeus
Common resident.

On farmland it is not numerous and can be of rather patchy distribution perhaps because of site preference. Certainly it likes a laneside site with a grass verge and a ditch as compared, say, with a thin hedge division between two arable fields in a farm's hinterland. An open aspect especially on high ground is also preferred.

Certain to be found on heathland, this species is also a woodland dweller if there is sufficient open space. It can manage quite well in the birch-bracken complex as long as there is some open sky, and it has taken over the conifer areas where there are new plantings or where the rides converge to produce the open aspect. In such situations small colonies may occur which, evened out, give a density of 6–8 pairs per 100 acres, placing it with the chiffchaff, whitethroat and greenfinch.

Corn bunting   Emberiza calandra Linnaeus
Fairly common resident.

For once, we have a simple, straightforward species of the field type and belonging to the farmland.

Both Sterland, who called it the common bunting, and Whitaker considered it reasonably common on cultivated land. Whitaker remarked that this bird preferred hedges on the roadside which bordered corn or seed fields. In TVBW times it has been noted as a lover of the roadside, especially where telegraph poles and wires provided vantage points. However, it is quite at home away from the roads in those open areas which suit it.

The TVBW carried out 2 surveys of this species in 1943 and 1958. It was found that the corn bunting in Nottinghamshire showed a marked preference for arable (especially corn) land. Distribution findings were: *Carrlands*—generally distributed on arable. *Bunter Sandstone*—although well-wooded, widespread small pockets of corn buntings were found on the cornland. *Trent Valley and tributary valleys*—common, and birds had spread to the high ground, eg Dorkett Head, Robin Hood and Mosley Hills. *Keuper Marl upland*—generally distributed in the south, but very few reported from East Markham northwards where small fields and tall hedges were thought to have an adverse effect. *South of the Trent Valley*—only a few on the Wolds, but well-distributed on the Trent Hills and the area bordering the Vale of Belvoir. *Eastern Notts*—hardly any from Langar to Cotham.

Since the above surveys, arable land (especially corn) has increased at the expense of the grassland, which coupled with the trend to larger fields should favour an extension to this species' range.

The density of the corn bunting is difficult to assess because of its habit of living in scattered colonies. 2 pairs per 100 acres gives some indication.

Black-headed bunting   Emberiza melanocephala Scopoli
Rare vagrant.
    2 records, 1886, 1966.

Cirl bunting   Emberiza cirlus Linnaeus
Rare vagrant.
    15 or so records, probably 6 reports, Whitaker; 9 reports, 1944-73, TVBW.

Ortolan bunting   Emberiza hortulana Linnaeus
Rare passage migrant.
    4 records, 1858, 1945, 1950, 1971.

Little bunting   Emberiza pusilla Pallas
Rare passage migrant.
    1 in 1950.

Reed bunting   Emberiza schoeniclus (Linnaeus)
Common resident. Some evidence of movement.
    This species has been found breeding on heathland, farmland and in forestry plantations during the last 10 years, suggesting an expansion in breeding habitat, but none the less the reed bunting is still very much a bird of the waterside. Its range in Nottinghamshire is shown by the map of streams and rivers, plus marshy places away from the main water-courses. Wherever a wet place is created, eg a gravel pit, and aquatic vegetation appears, so will the reed bunting. Naturally, it will occur in considerable numbers where the habitat is extensive, such as at the Attenborough Nature Reserve (c 100 pairs, 1969, Hornby) and will be restricted to 1 pair beside a farm pond, say of 200 square yards.
    There is a little evidence of movement, such as the departure of some of the local immature birds and females to the south-west. Also birds from northern areas have been caught as if they

were passage migrants between their breeding areas and a more southern wintering area.

Lapland bunting Calcarius lapponicus (Linnaeus)
Rare vagrant.
   1 in 1850 (Felkin).

Snow bunting Plectrophenax nivalis (Linnaeus)
Rare winter visitor, irregular.
   21 reports, 1950–73.
   The inclusive dates for this bird are 24 September to 4 March. November shows up as a good arrival month (TVBW records).

House sparrow Passer domesticus (Linnaeus)
Abundant resident.
   This species is not counted by census workers, chiefly because of the difficulty and the time involved. It is impossible to have an English farm without its chirping 'spuggies' and the holiday-making flocks in the corn are also an indication of numbers. For density this successful bird must be close on the heels of the 3 commonest species of the farmland, and possibly in some areas it is the most numerous. It is, of course, an abundant species about the dwellings of man, especially in the built-up areas.
   It is not entirely sedentary.

Tree sparrow Passer montanus (Linnaeus)
Common resident.
   This trim, alert sparrow is widespread about our county's farmland. Autumn flocks give a better indication of numbers than does the difficult sorting out of this species from the many house sparrows at other times of the year. At times these communal gatherings of tree sparrows reach four figures, and the ringing of 850 from c 1,000 in 1959 on the Nottingham Sewage Farm produced local recoveries, eg at Oxton, during the following breeding season.
   It is felt that numbers on any farm are controlled to some extent

by the availability of nest holes. Density from our small sample suggests 3-4 pairs per 100 acres, but it could be higher in some areas.

Although a field species, this hole-nesting bird comes to the woods like the starlings for breeding purposes, and in the smaller woods of the farmland it can be quite numerous. Good numbers frequent the ancient oaks of the Birklands, for instance. It is possible, remembering the insect-gathering ability of this sparrow, that some become truly woodland birds while feeding their young.

Random samples of different woodlands produced extremely variable results depending on the age of the trees and the presence or lack of nest holes. A large wood of secondary growth will hold only a few pairs while a 40-acre shelter belt of over-mature trees, full of holes and crannies, can carry up to 20 pairs.

Our ringers have found this species using sand martin holes for breeding.

TEMPORARY RESIDENTS

Escaped species which have resided within the county temporarily have included:

Carolina or wood duck	*Aix sponsa*
Chiloe wigeon	*Anas sibilatrix*
Bar-headed goose	*Anser indicus*
Black swan	*Cygnus atratus*
Demoiselle crane	*Anthropoides virgo*
Sacred ibis	*Threskiornis aethiopicus*
Flamingo species	

PAST RECORDS

Species recorded in the past, but unacceptable for the county include:

Whiskered tern   Chlidonias hybrida
Recorded by Oates as having occurred at Besthorpe, but lacked date and details.

Eagle owl   Bubo bubo (Linnaeus)
1 shot, 1908. Not accepted as genuinely wild at the time, because individuals had been released in the country.

Black woodpecker   Dryocopus martius
2 shot, Nottingham, undated (Whitaker) and sight reports of single birds, Park Hall and Harlow Wood, 1907. Not accepted at the time as truly wild, ie birds of this species had been released in the country.

White-winged crossbill   Loxia leucoptera (Gmelin)
2 shot (Felkin) went to the collection of Sir William Milner, Nunappleton, Yorkshire. As they were shot just after 5 parrot crossbills were killed by a Mr H. Wells (seemingly a professional bird-shooter), it is probable that these so-called white-winged of North America were the two-barred crossbill of Europe, which had figured in a westerly irruption.

Spanish sparrow   Passer hispaniolensis (Temminck)
Whitaker gives a full account of one which was obtained from a flock of house sparrows. He could see no reason why it had not found its way to England as many other chance species have done. It was during the autumn of 1900 at Wilford and, as one was accepted for Lundy in 1966, perhaps a fresh look at this record will be made by someone of the BOU.

REFERENCES

Bell, B. D., Catchpole, C. K. and Corbett, K. J. 'Problems of
Censusing Reed Buntings, Sedge Warblers and Reed Warblers',
Bird Study, 15: 43–52 (1968) and personal reports

Dobbs, A. 'Rook Numbers in Nottinghamshire over 35 years',
British Birds, 57: 360–4 (1964)

Dobbs, A. and Lamb, E. T. 'The Arrival of Chiffchaffs and Willow
Warblers in Nottinghamshire from 1954 to 1963', *Report on the
Birds of Nottinghamshire* (1964)

Docksey, A. I. H. and Roebuck, A. 'Census of Nottinghamshire
Rookeries, 1944', *Report on the Birds of Nottinghamshire* (1945)

Edwards, K. C. *The Land of Britain, Part 60, Nottinghamshire*
(1944)

Edwards, K. C. *Nottingham and its Region* (1966)

References

Felkin, W. 'A List of the Birds of Nottinghamshire', *Nottingham Hand Book* (1866)

Flegg, J. M. and Cox, C. J. 'Movement of Black-headed Gulls from Colonies in England and Wales', *Bird Study*, 19: 228–40 (1972)

Forestry Commission. *Woodland Statistics—Nottinghamshire* (1913, 1924, 1938, 1942, 1947–49)

Griffiths, M. E. 'The Population Density of the Kestrel in Leicestershire', *Bird Study*, 14: 184–90 (1967)

Hornby, R. J. 'Aspects of Population Ecology in the Reed Bunting' (Personal, 1971)

Ministry of Agriculture & Fisheries. *Farming Statistics—Nottinghamshire* (1866–1970)

Ministry of Agriculture & Fisheries. *Woodland Statistics—Nottinghamshire* (1932)

Nottingham Natural Science Field Club. *Bird Records* (1911–39)

Nottinghamshire Trust for Nature Conservation Ltd. *A Survey of Woodlands* (1971)

Oates, W. G. 'Notes of the Birds of Besthorpe' (unpublished) (1924)

Parslow, J. L. F. 'Changes in Status among Breeding Birds in Britain and Ireland', *British Birds*, 60: 20–1; 114–15 (1967)

Potts, G. R. 'Recent Changes in Farmland Fauna with special reference to the Decline of the Grey Partridge', *Bird Study*, 17: 145–66 (1970)

Roebuck, A. 'A Survey of Rooks in the Midlands', *British Birds*, 27: 4–23 (1933)

Southern, H. N. 'The Spread of the Swallow over Europe during the Spring', Witherby's *Handbook*, 2: 229 (1945)

Sterland, W. J. *The Birds of Sherwood Forest* (1869)

Ticehurst, N. F. and Jourdain, F. C. R. 'On the Distribution of the Nightingale during the Breeding Season in Great Britain', *British Birds*, 5: 2–21 (1912)

Trent River Board. *Diagrammatic Maps of the River Trent and its Principal Tributaries* (1952–70)

Whitaker, J. *Notes on the Birds of Nottinghamshire* (1907)

Whitaker, J. Unpublished notes (1907–30)

Whitlock, F. B. *Check-list of Nottinghamshire Birds* (1893)

ACKNOWLEDGEMENTS

In order to improve matters and also to speed up production, various members of the Society were asked to help; others outside the Society also contributed, and sincere acknowledgement is made to:

Jack Lever for combining the records of Sterland, Whitaker, Whitlock and the TVBW for the first draft of the systematic bird list, for discovering Felkin's list of 1866, and for reading the manuscript copy as a member of the Book Committee; Peter Saunders for reading the manuscript and for advice as a member of the Book Committee; Leavers Howitt for work on the early Nottinghamshire ornithologists; Paul Hope who, from his experience in forestry, was able to give an expert viewpoint as regards woodland management and birds.

Summarising dates is a slow, exacting business and thanks go to Margot Payne for making charts on the arrival of the summer visitors, to Michael Powell for the wader-migration details extracted from the TVBW annual reports, and to Mr and Mrs T. Lawrence for work on Whitaker's notes.

Aid in illustrating the chapters came from several sources. Ruth Nettleship skilfully prepared the maps on the topographical features, the county's woodland, graded surface drainage and the county map. Alan Howarth helped with the prototype distribution maps for nightjar, lesser spotted woodpecker, willow tit, nuthatch and redstart. Bill Woods created the small bird illustrations, while Brian Gadsby provided the supporting bird photographs.

We are grateful to Rhona Dalton for typing the chapters on the Woodland and Wetland Species, and for help with part of the final systematic bird list.

The help of the Curators and their assistants of the Libraries and Museums of Wollaton Hall, Newark and Mansfield, and the successful delving by the Librarians of the City Library and the County Library are acknowledged with full appreciation. James Ferguson-Lees receives our thanks for allowing access to all past numbers of *British Birds*.

We are grateful also to the Forestry Commission, the Nature Conservancy, the Nottinghamshire Trust for Nature Conservation and the Trent River Authority for information supplied. Assistance from the many landowners or their agents is also gratefully acknowledged.

Austen Dobbs
Bulcote, 1973

INDEX